— Praise for —

Motivational Interviewing for Mental Health Clinicians

"Frey and Hall have done something remarkable: added something entirely new to the MI world. Literally breathing life into the heartset of learning MI, this toolkit gently guides practitioners into a self-reflective and compassionate review of their practice and learning MI. Mental health providers have another must-add book for their libraries."

-David B. Rosengren, PhD,
President & CEO, Prevention Research Institute,
Author of *Building Motivational Interviewing Skills: A Practitioner Workbook*

"*Motivational Interviewing for Mental Health Clinicians* provides the tools you need to integrate the skills and strategies of motivational interviewing (MI) into your day-to-day work. Offering a cornucopia of activities, exercises, and invitations to self-reflection, Frey and Hall are expert guides to putting in place the building blocks of an MI practice that fits you and feels like yours. Speaking in a friendly, encouraging, and knowledgeable voice, they invite you to join them in a step-by-step process of thinking about what you do—its challenges as well as its successes—and trying out new ideas and approaches for enhancing motivation and commitment to change. They will help you deepen your empathy for your clients, your compassion for their struggles, and your celebration of their triumphs—and help you feel more like the practitioner you want to be. With examples galore of conversations about all kinds of problems in all kinds of settings, *Motivational Interviewing for Mental Health Clinicians* is a practical, concrete resource for every practitioner who wants to master the MI way of being with people."

-Allan Zuckoff, PhD,
Author of *Finding Your Way to Change: How the Power of Motivational Interviewing Can Reveal What You Want and Help You Get There*

"This is a refreshing and fun book that is a great resource for busy clinicians and anyone wanting to improve, practice, or hone their MI skills in a purposeful, practical, and effective way. There's a nice combination of didactics, client-practitioner scenarios/dialogues, and case examples, along with practitioner exercises peppered expertly throughout each chapter for on-the-spot skill practice. This is a book I can pick up after a long day and become energized to utilize these strategies with my clientele. The activities are practical and able to be completed in reasonable amount of time."

-Nikki Cockern, PhD, LLP,
Clinical Psychologist, Clinical Manager, Assistant Professor, Wayne State University

"Being a trainer who has done numerous trainings on mental health, I found the practitioner exercises, especially for the MI spirit, extremely practical. I can see myself using that format for my training presentations. The exercises are new and address the real content of MI. Great book!"

-**Maurice Bulls, MEd**,
Executive Director, Behavior Change Consulting Institute

"This is a highly relevant and user-friendly package of resources for which I've been awaiting for a decade. It will be an indispensable resource in my work to further support my interprofessional teams to incorporate MI knowledge and skills in outpatient, inpatient, and crisis settings. It will occupy a prominent place in my professional library."

-**Tim Godden, BSc, BAA(J), BSW, MSW**,
Clinical Supervisor and Trainer, Toronto, Canada

"This book has a clear, simple, direct style that belies its sophistication. It would be a good adjunct to an organized program of MI instruction for practitioners in the mental health field, but is also clear enough that it would work for independent study. There's enough detail and nuance in it that intermediate/advanced learners would also benefit from it as well as people just starting out with MI. My favorite thing about the book is the range of examples: it's often said that there are 'many right ways' to do MI, but there are few books that actively demonstrate this as well as this one, something that reflects the years of experience the authors have had as MI trainers."

-**Guy Undrill, MB ChB PhD**,
Retired Consultant Psychiatrist, Gloucestershire Health and Care NHS Foundation Trust

MOTIVATIONAL INTERVIEWING

FOR MENTAL HEALTH CLINICIANS

A Toolkit for Skills Enhancement

Jennifer Frey, PhD and Ali Hall, JD

Foreword by William R. Miller, PhD

Published by
PESI Publishing
3839 White Ave
Eau Claire, WI 54703

Cover: Amy Rubenzer
Editing: Candace Baker, MSW
Layout: Amy Rubenzer & Bookmasters

ISBN: 9781683732013

PESI Publishing
pesipublishing.com

ABOUT THE AUTHORS

Jennifer Frey, PhD

Jen is a licensed psychologist practicing in Washington, DC. She is also a motivational interviewing (MI) consultant, trainer, and coach working with systems, organizations, and practitioners to improve service effectiveness. Jen has served in a number of clinical leadership roles including founding and running a homeless outreach team, supervising practitioners, implementing evidence-based practices, establishing communities of practice, and serving on the board of a youth services organization. She develops clinical protocols and publishes on program evaluation and implementation of evidence-based and best practices. She has been a member of the Motivational Interviewing Network of Trainers (MINT) since 1998. For additional information, please see https://motivationalinterviewing.org/profile/JenniferFrey.

Ali Hall, JD

Ali is a member of MINT and is an independent consultant and trainer. She designs and facilitates MI workshops in a wide variety of contexts and provides training for trainers in evidence-based practices. She is a codeveloper of the Motivational Interviewing Competency Assessment (MICA; Jackson, Butterworth, Hall, & Gilbert, 2015), a coding and coaching tool for MI skill improvement.

Ali completed her graduate studies in organizational behavior and work motivation at the School of Industrial and Labor Relations at Cornell University, and her JD at the Cornell University School of Law. In her spare time, Ali participates in marathon swimming events in order to raise funds for under-resourced kids' charities. For additional information, please see https://motivationalinterviewing.org/profile/AliHall.

DEDICATION

For Neil, whose friendship, love, and spirit makes life even better than I thought it could be.

For you, for taking this journey with us.
                    —JF

For LTH, whose love and perfect presence is everything.

For those we serve, whose growth always helps us along our individual and collective change journeys.
                    —AH

ACKNOWLEDGMENTS

There are so many people who have contributed to our work on this toolkit. We would like to thank Bill Miller, Steve Rollnick, Terri Moyers, Denise Ernst, and all the members of the MINT. You continually nurture and deepen our knowledge about MI and how to train others to use MI effectively. We would also like to thank the thousands of people we've trained and worked with over the years who have shaped our MI practice.

We would like to thank Karsyn Morse and Linda Jackson at PESI Publishing for all of your support. We have been so fortunate to get to work with you.

We would also like to thank our editor, Candace Baker, MSW. Your thorough work and dedication to reader-friendly content substantially improved this toolkit. Thank you!

TABLE OF CONTENTS

FOREWORD

It seems a bit ironic that it took so long for motivational interviewing (MI) to come to where its roots lie: in mental health and the pioneering work of Carl Rogers and his students (Miller & Moyers, 2017). In the 20th century, MI first found a home in addiction treatment, then in medical health care, and on to corrections and social work. Although both of MI's codevelopers are clinical psychologists, the first edition of MI in the Treatment of Psychological Problems was not published until 2008 (Arkowitz et al., 2008). I am therefore pleased to see MI coming home to mental/behavioral health applications.

This book is authored by two well-seasoned MI practitioners and trainers, Jen Frey and Ali Hall, both of whom have made significant contributions to the MI Network of Trainers (MINT). It is fair to say that MI is still relatively young in mental health applications, though research is accumulating rapidly. A challenge I often find when introducing MI to psychological and counseling practitioners is the perception that "I already know this. I already do this. It's just common factors in all counseling and psychotherapy." And there is some truth to this. Reviewing the 70-year literature on what makes therapists more effective (Miller & Moyers, 2021), we found strong overlap of these supposedly "common" or "non-specific" factors that improve client outcomes. The problem is that therapeutic skills like accurate empathy are not all that "common" in practice, though almost all therapists regard themselves (accurately or not) to be "good listeners." Neither are therapeutic skills that improve client outcomes "non-specific." They can be specified, measured, learned, taught, and linked in research to how clients fare after treatment. That's what we have been doing in MI research for almost 40 years.

An advantage of MI in clinical practice is that you need not be converted to a new school of therapy and abandon what you were doing before. MI is complementary to what else you do. Research is clear that when added to other active treatment methods, MI improves their efficacy. It's not something to do instead of tools like cognitive behavioral therapy. MI is a way of delivering other treatment methods, a way of being with your clients (Rogers, 1980). Therapists' measurable skills like accurate empathy make a substantial difference across schools of psychotherapy.

Something we have learned the hard way is that clinicians easily form an inaccurate belief that they are already doing MI and are skillful at it. Then we observe practice sessions using reliable coding tools, and the skills are often modest at best, not enough to make a difference in clients' outcomes. We have known for some time that a two-day MI workshop with me doesn't significantly improve practice, and any small gains in skill tend to degrade over time (Miller & Mount, 2001). It might be my own shortcomings as a teacher, but in general, clinical skills are not strengthened by warming a chair in a workshop. A training workshop is usually just the beginning of learning MI, consolidated by subsequent deliberate practice with feedback and coaching (Miller et al., 2004). There are large differences in client outcome among practitioners of MI (and of virtually every form of psychotherapy). It matters who delivers it, and we have been fascinated to study what accounts for these differences in delivering what is allegedly the same treatment.

So here you have a handbook of learning tools and dozens of practitioner exercises from which you can choose to strengthen your own clinical skillfulness when having conversations about change (which is mostly what I did throughout my career in treatment). Ambivalence is the normal human response when considering change, and it makes a large difference how you understand and respond to it. The expert trap—telling clients what to do and why they should do it—is a recipe for resistance and no change. The exercises in this book are designed to give you a deeper experiential understanding of MI. As the authors point out, these skills also have implications for your own wellness as a practitioner. With some guidance, you can learn how to learn MI. Your clients will teach you once you know what cues to watch for that tell you whether you're on the right or wrong track. Bon appétit with the large menu of practice methods here to help you strengthen your skills in MI.

William R. Miller, PhD
Emeritus Distinguished Professor of Psychology and Psychiatry
The University of New Mexico

PREFACE

We both learned about motivational interviewing (MI) as we worked to improve services for populations whose needs were not being addressed. Jen worked in a mental health clinic, studying the treatment of schizophrenia and co-occurring cocaine dependence at a time when the field was just beginning to think about treating mental health issues and substance use issues concurrently. Ali worked at a comprehensive residential treatment program for people who were homeless and experiencing chronic substance use issues.

Our early experiences incorporating MI into our practices were powerful enough to define our career paths. These are our stories.

JEN:

In the clinic, we were studying a combined MI and cognitive behavioral therapy (CBT) approach for people who were experiencing co-occurring schizophrenia and cocaine dependence. We knew that we wanted to apply MI to this work. We didn't know at the time how profoundly MI would impact people's lives.

The people we worked with were already participating in services with the ACT Team and the Homeless Outreach Team. We collaborated with these teams throughout the study to overcome the significant barriers to services this population experienced.

Our work focused on applying the principles (i.e., express empathy, roll with resistance, avoid argumentation, support self-efficacy, develop discrepancy) and core skills from Miller and Rollnick's first edition of *Motivational Interviewing* (1991). We learned together with the people we served about increasing treatment engagement, retention, medication adherence, abstinence, symptom management, and progress toward personal goals. Instead of *persuading* people to take medications and stop using substances, we expressed interest in *their* thoughts about their symptoms and experiences. We explored the role of medications and substances in their lives: "When you've taken this medication in the past, what happened to the voices you hear?" "When you use crack/cocaine, what happens with your thoughts about people breaking into your home?" As they explored what worked well for them and what worked less well, they made decisions that reduced symptom interference and opened up opportunities to make other changes in their lives. They taught us the value of sharing with them their growing list of negative weekly urine toxicology screens. They made it clear to us that affirmations of their effort and nonjudgmental responses to episodes of substance use increased their interest in continuing to work toward their goals, better symptom management, and abstinence.

We reflected and expressed interest in their self-motivational statements (change talk) about how their goals related to taking medication, reducing substance use, attending groups, and participating in recovery supports:

- "It's important to you to reconnect with your child, and you like this idea of writing a letter to her."
- "You are saying it is easier to stay in contact with your child when you have a stable place to live, are getting your shot, are attending groups, and are not using crack."
- "You're thinking it would help to find an NA meeting where you feel comfortable."

When we explored tools to support their recovery from substance use (e.g., drug refusal skills, assertiveness training, problem-solving skills, managing cravings, relaxation), we started with their experience and their challenges and tailored the information to them:

- "How is avoiding drug use helpful to you?"
- "So, you've noticed your symptoms are better when you aren't using. You want to stay sober so you can feel better. And staying sober helps you work toward reconnecting with your family."
- "When do you feel tempted to use?"
- "How do you stay sober in those situations?"
- "So, when you see someone you use with, it's hard to walk away. And you end up using with them. It sounds like you'd like to change that, to find some ways to avoid using."

Our genuine interest in their experience and goals conveyed our belief in their absolute worth and their expertise on their own lives. They responded by continuing to work with us (the first noticeable outcome of our work), improving their symptom management, and experiencing increased satisfaction with their lives. Adherence to medication and treatment increased and substance use decreased. Motivation to work toward personal goals (e.g., finding housing, reconnecting with family, gaining employment, engaging in self-care) increased. They transitioned from the ACT Team and the Homeless Outreach Team into outpatient services to maintain their progress and continue working toward their goals. MI helped us to partner well with the people we were serving and with other service providers.

One of the keys to our MI skill development during this time was holding regular team meetings where we listened to recordings of our sessions and practiced ways to approach challenging conversations. MI made doing the work easier, for both the people we served and our team. It was easier to collaborate and brought joy to our practice.

It's still true today. The more MI consistent my practice is, the more collaborative and joyful my work is.

ALI:

When I first learned of MI many years ago, I was working at a program where confrontation and persuasion were the cornerstones of behavioral health service delivery. Some of the things we were trained to say to the people we served (and were rewarded for saying) included:

- "What do you mean 'you think...'? Don't think! Your best thinking got you here!"
- "We have to break you down to build you up!"
- "Nothing you learned (in prison, on the street, etc.) is going to do you any good now. You've got to put it all behind you and start all over."

- "You're not motivated; why don't you just go back out there and try again when you're ready to change."

We cared deeply for the people we served and for our work. We wanted more than anything to relieve the suffering we saw in others. We wanted to engage with people; we wanted to make a difference. We wanted to fix things. To fix people. It was the righting reflex—from a genuine desire to help others—in full bloom. We were doing the best we could, based on our assumptions that others lacked insight, skills, and motivation, and that it was our job to provide those things.

When those we served disagreed with us or were unsure about changes we thought were good for them, we called them "resistant," "in denial," or "difficult." When they told us one thing and did another, we labeled them as "unmotivated" or "manipulative." Not surprisingly, they were often angry, shutdown, or less than honest because they knew they were facing our inevitable judgment!

Some people we served were ultimately successful in making the changes they desired. However, knowing what I now know about behavior change, I believe it is likely that those particular individuals would have made changes under any circumstances. But back then, we attributed *their* successes to *our* treatment.

More often, people left treatment discouraged, invalidated, and re-traumatized. They struggled to make the changes they really wanted to, or they returned all the more strongly committed to painful and difficult lifestyles that helped in many ways to soften their pain—but that also generated more. Although we blamed them for having insufficient motivation, I am quite sure that confrontation, persuasion, and judgment—as well-intentioned as it may have been—drove them away. Some people we served gave us relevant feedback:

- "I know you care about me, but I don't think you understand me. I don't think you support me."
- "You don't get how hard this is for me."
- "I've been hearing this stuff all my life, that I'm not good enough and don't have the skills to make it."
- "I just want to go back to jail; at least people respected me there."
- "This is just like the emotional abuse and control my father put me through."

Clearly, our approach was less than adequate. MI could not have arrived at a more fortuitous time, not only for the benefit of the people we served, but for us as well. We set about creating a program with MI at the forefront; a program that supported an individual's autonomy, encouraged collaboration, and helped them make the changes *they* desired. The response from the people we served was extraordinary: They exhibited greater academic success, found stable housing, obtained and maintained a living wage, reduced their use of drugs and alcohol, and enhanced their overall mental health.

Introducing MI helped us, too: Working *with* others was much less exhausting than wrestling with them. We no longer had to shoulder the burden of being the only expert in the room. It turned out that giving people the opportunity to bring their expertise and capacity to the table got us further, and faster.

How did we make that shift in how we treated others? To begin with, we found a way to be a welcome, invited part of their change journey. We changed our view of them, our expectations for them, and our hope and optimism for them. We began to believe that those we served already had the capacity and potential for change and that our job was to bring that forward so that it could flourish. When we talked to people in the program, we started to sound like:

- "You've got a lot of thoughts about this. I'm interested to hear your ideas."
- "What would you find helpful?"
- "I can offer some resources, if you like, and you can tell me what you think you'd like to do. These decisions really belong to you."
- "With all you've been through, what strengths and skills have been most useful for you? What are some of the successes you've experienced that can help you here?"
- "You're really motivated to get this probation behind you—I can see how determined you are to make that happen. How can I be helpful to you for that?"

Following that early MI experience, my learning journey continued by providing support to programs, practitioners, and those we served across a wide variety of contexts. I have yet to encounter a setting in which both practitioners and those they serve did not benefit from MI spirit and skills.

INTRODUCTION

A large body of research supports our positive experiences. This toolkit is an extension of our commitment to advancing the use of MI in mental health settings through training, coaching, and mentoring practitioners. We sincerely hope you find it useful in your own journey.

A NOTE ABOUT PRONOUNS

We use "they," "their," and "them" even when talking about a single person. This avoids the awkward use of "he or she," and is more gender inclusive.

LEARNING EXPERIENCES IN THE TOOLKIT

This toolkit on motivational interviewing (MI) is designed for mental health practitioners who have had introductory training in MI and are already implementing it into their practices. It is *not* a primer on MI. MI skill development is not a time-limited event. Skills drift over time, and practitioners' proficiency varies from change conversation to change conversation. The toolkit is designed to guide ongoing learning, practice, and efforts to better integrate MI into your services. To meet these goals, the toolkit offers three types of learning experiences:

 Practitioner Exercises

 Partner Exercises

 Practitioner Tools

Practitioner Exercises provide opportunities for you to explore and reflect on fundamental concepts, spirit, and skills of MI. We often ask you to consider how an MI concept or skill applies to your current practice, what intentions you may have to use it more frequently, and how you might choose to use it in your next session. Some exercises allow you to apply your learning even more intentionally by asking you to provide your own ideas of appropriate MI responses within a particular conversation.

You can do these exercises on your own or you might want to collaborate with a colleague to discuss and support each other in applying MI concepts, spirit, or skills to situations you encounter in your work. You could also use these exercises as opportunities to collaborate with a team of coworkers to consider the goals of your services and how your agency might become even more consistent with MI practice.

Partner Exercises are those that will be most effective when practiced with a colleague. However, we recognize that many MI practitioners will choose to use this toolkit as part of their own independent journey for deepening their skills. For some it's a matter of necessity, for some it's a learning style. You know what will work best for you.

Practitioner Tools are actual tools you can clip or copy out of the toolkit to use in your work. Some tools help you create job aids and some you can use with the people you serve. You may want to discuss the tools with colleagues to assess how they could best work in your practice.

> The Motivational Interviewing Network of Trainers website offers a glossary of MI terms.

MAXIMIZING YOUR LEARNING

Conversations about change are naturally challenging. We recommend that you practice applying the spirit of MI to challenging conversations about change with colleagues on a regular basis. We hope this toolkit gives you some ideas for practice.

We also recommend working with an experienced MI coach who offers objective and reliable feedback. Getting this type of feedback can help you decide the next steps for integrating MI into your personal style and improving your service outcomes. Experienced MI coaches tailor feedback and practice to help you shift your current practice to embody the MI spirit.

Feedback, coaching, and practice will help you develop proficiency in MI more quickly and will increase the effectiveness of your conversations about change. While this toolkit is not a substitute for high-quality feedback and coaching, it is designed to support your ongoing practice of MI and help you explore how to apply MI to your work. Chapter 10 will provide more information about ways to help you deepen your practice (e.g., direct observation, coaching, coding, communities of practice).

Many exercises require writing. Although some space is provided in the toolkit, you will want to have a notebook handy to extend your answers if necessary.

Beginner's Mind

A *beginner's mind* is a place of openness, eagerness, a lack of preconceptions, and a gentleness with ourselves. Deepening our MI skills—as might be the case for any skill set or model—asks us to embrace a beginner's mind, even if we've been practicing for quite some time. We acknowledge that we are in a constant process of development and improvement. *Flawlessness is unrealistic!*

It is impossible to begin to learn that which one thinks one already knows.

—Epictetus

A beginner's mind is a learner's mind, and in MI we are always "learning to learn" how to be genuinely helpful. Across all disciplines, a learning-to-learn approach is reinforced by:

- Identifying benefits of the skill set ("This can help the people I work with in these ways..." or "This can help me as a practitioner in these ways...").
- Honest self-awareness (receiving coaching and feedback about our MI skills).
- Finding ways to increase meaningful self-evaluation, to know where we're at, what we're doing well, and what we can do differently.
- Curiosity ("I wonder how I can work together more effectively with the people participating in my services").
- Vulnerability ("I recognize I am trying something afresh, and it may be awkward for a bit, so I may not feel fully confident as I do with 'business as usual'").

It can help to have some compassion for ourselves as we try new things in the context of our already demanding lives. Cultivating self-compassion and taking the pressure off ourselves to be flawless is also a way of recognizing that we are still and always will be unfolding.

PRACTICING BEGINNER'S MIND

• • • • • •

Please take a moment to provide some self-reflective responses to the following questions.

How will learning and practicing MI benefit the people I work with?

_____

_____

_____

_____

_____

How will learning and practicing MI help me as a professional? As a person?

_____

_____

_____

_____

_____

What ideas do I have for working with people even more effectively? What could I try?

_____

_____

_____

_____

_____

How can I keep myself going on my learning journey, even when it is tempting to maintain "business as usual"?

_____

_____

_____

_____

_____

How can I show compassion for myself as a learner on an important journey?

_____

_____

_____

_____

_____

What am I already doing to support my continued learning and skills development?

_____

_____

_____

_____

_____

THE ONE-MINUTE MI CHECKUP

• • • • • •

Can we really improve our MI skillfulness one minute at a time? Absolutely! As you work through this toolkit, we encourage you to keep this "One-Minute Checkup" in mind. Make copies of this page so that you can continue to use it. You can add new options to it over time and track your growth.

What one MI-consistent behavior did I use well today?

_____

_____

_____

_____

_____

What opportunity to use an MI-consistent skill might I have missed today?

_____

_____

_____

_____

_____

What is one MI-consistent behavior I want to try tomorrow?

_____

_____

_____

_____

_____

MI WITH PEOPLE EXPERIENCING MENTAL HEALTH ISSUES

People possess substantial personal expertise and wisdom regarding themselves and tend to develop in a positive direction if given proper conditions of support.

—Miller & Moyers, 2006

IN THIS CHAPTER

- The Value of MI in Mental Health Settings
- MI with People Experiencing:
  - Depression
  - Anxiety
  - Bipolar Symptoms
  - Substance Use Issues
  - Thought Disorders

In this chapter, we describe how you can use MI to support people experiencing mental health issues. We address service provision in dedicated mental health and general settings, and pay particular attention to depression, anxiety, bipolar, substance use, and thought disorder. We did not include personality disorders in this book because there is little research on this area of MI right now (though there is the promise of more to come). However, we have found in our own work with people with personality disorders that high-quality MI conversations can increase engagement and intrinsic motivation for change in this population.

MI is used in mental health settings to increase service effectiveness through enhancing engagement, retention, and long-term behavior change. We hope that this chapter and the chapters that follow inspire your own ideas in delivering effective interventions tailored to the needs and strengths of the people you serve.

THE VALUE OF MI IN MENTAL HEALTH SETTINGS

A large number of MI clinical trials have focused on engaging and treating people experiencing a broad range of mental health issues and combinations of issues. The MINT website maintains a bibliography of more than 1,500 MI trials involving both youth and adults.

MI also has been integrated with other evidence-based interventions (e.g., CBT, behavioral activation, interpersonal therapy) to improve treatment outcomes and reduce symptom recurrence (Balán, Lejuez, Hoffer, & Blanco, 2016; Naar & Flynn, 2015; Naar & Safren, 2017; Zuckoff, Swartz, & Grote, 2015).

Mental health services are provided in many settings and not everyone enters treatment by choice or because they recognize a need for change. MI is particularly helpful when working with people who are reluctant to engage in mental health services and/or distrust mental health practitioners. This reluctance stems from many sources, including:

- Past experiences with practitioners and services.
- Trauma.
- Stigma associated with mental disorder diagnoses and treatment.
- Feeling unwelcome or fearful in mental health service settings.
- Ambivalence about change (e.g., "my anxiety protects my family from harm").
- Reluctance to explore feelings of pain, sadness, anxiety, shame, hopelessness, helplessness.
- Fear of judgment.

MI offers a variety of ways to engage and show our willingness to understand, even in the initial stages, when it can be difficult to know if we are connecting. As practitioners, we work to create a *safe space*—one characterized by respect and collaboration—within which people can explore their own interests, experiences, and good ideas for change.

MI is not done *to* people, nor is it a way of *getting* people to change. Rather, it is a way of guiding a conversation that engages people by looking together at their experiences, strengths, values, skills, and goals. As the person hears themselves talk about potential directions for change, their interest in making such changes increases. We work together to resolve ambivalence and increase momentum toward actual change. MI helps us invite people to:

- Expand their goals from surviving day-to-day to having a satisfying and meaningful life, even when symptoms are severe and persist.
- Identify and address the stigma and other barriers they experience in everyday life.
- Appreciate their own innate wisdom, skills, values, and goals and guide their discovery of their own options for change.

In contrast to an "expert-patient" or traditional advice-giving approach, MI emphasizes accurate empathy and the person's perspective. The practitioner and person are partners working together toward the person's change goals with the person as the expert in their own recovery process.

Mental health issues are often complex. A person is not just depressed; they also have specific ideas about why events happened to them, what triggers their symptoms, what will help them feel better, and what their options are for better health. A person who is anxious may want to relieve their distress and, at the same time, may feel unwilling to practice recommended strategies. A person who is homeless may refuse to cross a physical threshold (e.g., into a clinic) for services but be willing to meet with practitioners who provide services in the community. MI offers helpful ways to navigate these conversations by honoring the person's perceptions, experiences, and preferences while exploring possible options for change.

MI helps us to offer compassion, empathy, collaboration, and autonomy support while working with people who are navigating their own recovery journey. For example, when people respond to questions with irritation or by shutting down or becoming overwhelmed, we have effective skills for rebuilding the working alliance, reengaging, or offering options that are easier to understand.

MI practitioners guide and deepen understanding of a person's intentions, strengths, and experience using reflections and affirmations. This collaborative stance avoids intrusive advice giving and opinions that intensify symptoms and create discord (i.e., a rupture in our interpersonal dynamic). This approach also supports our work with other treatment practitioners, family members, and social networks.

MI has been studied with a variety of populations with mental health issues. The following sections offer a basic rationale and some specific considerations for using MI with people experiencing depression, anxiety, bipolar issues, substance use issues, and thought disorders. Further, the entire toolkit is about using MI with these populations, and you will find numerous examples and exercises that relate to each of these disorders. Chapter 9 offers a detailed look at MI with people who are contemplating suicide.

DEPRESSION

People experiencing depression report the most benefit from treatment involving a strong working alliance, autonomy support, and active collaboration in deciding the focus of treatment interventions and planning. They experience increased mastery and improved functioning through pacing (i.e., guiding a process that is not too fast or too slow), structured activities to address ambivalence and barriers, and goals that incorporate meaningful roles in the community (Bradshaw, Roseborough, & Armour, 2006; Richardson & Barkham, 2017). MI increases treatment engagement, retention, and completion of between-session activities by addressing specific challenges including (Balán et al., 2016; Naar & Flynn, 2015; Naar & Safren, 2017; Zuckoff et al., 2015):

- Increasing motivation to feel better by increasing self-confidence and optimism for life goals. ("I'd like to be able to spend time with people who are important to me. Being calmer, more patient with my kids, and feeling less sad will help with that.")

- Increasing engagement in treatment by decreasing the focus on problems and increasing the focus on removing barriers to goals and living according to personal values. ("I'd like to feel up to going out." "I'd like to do something more meaningful.")

- Increasing treatment follow-through (e.g., retention, completion of between-session activities) by increasing the focus on autonomy, addressing fluctuating motivation for treatment, and collaborating on ways to remove barriers to life goals. ("I guess I'm feeling better on some days, but I'd like to feel better all the time.")

- Increasing involvement in education about depression and coping skills designed to address depression. ("Ideally, I'd like to never feel depressed again, but now I understand that I can prevent a complete spiral down and maintain my important relationships.")

MI is a helpful stand-alone treatment for addressing depression related to other issues (e.g., physical conditions). Outcomes include increased self-efficacy for managing health conditions and decreased depression and high-risk behaviors. Brief approaches (generally up to four sessions) use MI spirit, core skills, and strategies to increase awareness of risky health behaviors (e.g., irregular medication follow-through, substance use, risky sexual practices), and intrinsic motivation and confidence for making a change.

MI complements other depression treatment approaches by focusing on treatment engagement and follow-through, increasing intrinsic motivation and confidence for change, and emphasizing treatment relationship factors. Some specific ways MI increases depression treatment engagement and follow-through include:

- Evoking the person's concerns, values, and goals.
- Offering options for treatment interventions (e.g., medication, psychotherapy, rewarding activities, problem solving).
- Exploring information about depression and specific interventions.
- Increasing hope and confidence for managing symptoms and working toward longer term stability.

YOUR WORK WITH PEOPLE EXPERIENCING DEPRESSION

· · · · · ·

What strategies are you already using in your work with people who experience depression?

_____

_____

_____

_____

_____

What has worked well for you?

_____

_____

_____

_____

_____

What supports (e.g., policies and procedures, supervision, MI training) does your organization offer for working with this population?

_____

_____

_____

_____

_____

ANXIETY

MI increases the effectiveness of anxiety treatment as a stand-alone treatment, a prelude to treatment, or integrated with other evidence-based practices, such as CBT (Marcus, Westra, Angus, & Kertes, 2011; Westra & Arkowitz, 2010; Westra & Constantino, 2019). Anxiety treatment often involves exposure to feared situations without the avoidance strategies the person usually uses to feel safe and in control. Profound ambivalence about engaging in treatment, exposure-related interventions, changing anxiety-related behaviors, and following through with between-session activities is common. People experiencing anxiety may say things like:

- "I'm just not convinced that treatment is going to help."
- "If I stop worrying, my kids will think I don't love them anymore. I'm not sure I can do this."
- "My worrying really interferes with my life, but it helps me protect my family from harm. If I stop worrying, I won't be prepared when something happens."
- "I can't stand the anxiety anymore, but I just can't expose myself to x; I feel like I will die if I do."

When people are distressed about their anxiety, it is easy to miss their ambivalence about treatment engagement and change. Instead of understanding and respecting the person's concerns, the common response to statements like these is to start exploring how the person might make a start. Profound ambivalence quickly becomes discord when we press for treatment engagement, behavior change, and/or interventions (Westra, Constantino, & Aviram, 2011). For example:

Practitioner: "Tell me about what you do now to relax when you start worrying."

Person [quickly]: "Um, I don't know… I worry. I try to work out a solution. It's pretty intense."

Practitioner: "Well, you mentioned smoking as a way to calm down and…"

Person [interrupting]: "Well, I don't think so, maybe when I started smoking, but not now."

Practitioner: "Well, I was just thinking of the connection between taking the time to smoke and relaxing."

Person [disagreeing, "yes-but"]: "Um, yeah, no… I mean at first, yes, but now, no, I don't think so. I'm still anxious, even when I'm smoking."

When opposition emerges in conversations about change, it predicts poorer treatment outcomes. Exploring sustain talk about anxiety behaviors with acceptance and compassion supports development of rapport and openness to change (Sijercic, Button, Westra, & Hara, 2016). MI helps us work with the person to build their sense of self-confidence and motivation for facing fears and reduce their reliance on avoidance behaviors. People recovering from anxiety report that they benefit the most from empathic practitioners who offer a safe space in which to understand their experiences first and then explore potential changes and next steps (Westra & Arkowitz, 2010).

YOUR WORK WITH PEOPLE EXPERIENCING ANXIETY

· · · · · ·

What strategies are you already using in your work with people who experience anxiety?

_____

_____

_____

_____

_____

What has worked well for you?

_____

_____

_____

_____

_____

What supports (e.g., policies and procedures, supervision, MI training) does your organization offer for working with this population?

_____

_____

_____

_____

_____

BIPOLAR SYMPTOMS

As with depression and anxiety, MI is being integrated into treatment approaches for bipolar issues (e.g., family psychoeducation, medication management, cognitive behavioral relapse prevention, interpersonal, and social rhythm therapy). Bipolar experiences can be intense and distressing with onsets that vary from a gradually increasing sense that something is wrong, to a sudden terrifying sense of total breakdown. Functioning varies widely and it can take up to 10 years before receiving an accurate diagnosis and effective treatment (Hirschfeld, Lewis, & Vornik, 2003; Suppes et al., 2001). Difficulty communicating these experiences to family, friends, and practitioners intensifies a person's feelings of confusion, isolation, and being misunderstood (Veseth, Binder, Borg, & Davidson, 2013):

- "Why do I feel this way?"
- "Why is everything suddenly so dull?"
- "Why are my thoughts and feelings racing?"

Misunderstandings sometimes lead to misdiagnosis and treatment that triggers a worsening of the symptoms (e.g., antidepressants triggering a manic episode). Symptom recurrence rates are estimated at up to two episodes per year following treatment (Tondo, Vázquez, & Baldessarini, 2017). MI increases the effectiveness of evidence-based treatment and recurrence prevention approaches by strengthening understanding of the person's experiences and wisdom about themselves. Bipolar-related experiences are often chaotic and deeply painful, creating profound ambivalence about engaging in treatment, changing behaviors that sometimes feel good, and following through with between-session activities:

- "But I like it when I feel good. I like the energy. I get so much done. I've been able to focus on my work and I get a lot of good ideas."
- "My life takes a hit when I'm depressed, and I need the extra energy to make everything right again. To get back to my full strength—be as well as I can be."
- I have nothing to look forward to. I've lost everything."

MI supports the person in resolving their own ambivalence by valuing the person as the expert on their own experience, developing a deeper understanding of how the person's experiences are related to life changes and stressors, and tailoring recurrence prevention options to be consistent with the person's goals and values. Discord is likely to emerge when people are pressed to accept a particular diagnosis, medication, or treatment approach:

- "I can't accept this diagnosis. They will all think I am like my brother. I won't accept it."
- "It really wasn't that bad. I think everyone is overreacting. My parents don't need to come in for that meeting. It's a waste of their time."
- "No, I don't agree with you. I don't want to take medications. I've worked hard and I deserve to feel really good for a while."

People in recovery from bipolar experiences report the greatest benefit from working with practitioners who maintain a strongly connected and collaborative style, support autonomy, and offer information about treatment options that are consistent with the person's values and goals (Bilderbeck, Saunders, Price, & Goodwin, 2014).

YOUR WORK WITH PEOPLE EXPERIENCING BIPOLAR SYMPTOMS

· · · · · ·

What strategies are you already using in your work with people who experience bipolar symptoms?

_____

_____

_____

_____

_____

What has worked well for you?

_____

_____

_____

_____

_____

What supports (e.g., policies and procedures, supervision, MI training) does your organization offer for working with this population?

_____

_____

_____

_____

_____

SUBSTANCE USE ISSUES

Whether or not we are aware of it, we are likely treating people who are experiencing negative effects of substance use (Miller, Forcehimes, & Zweben, 2019). MI helps us address substance use issues and combines well with other evidence-based approaches (e.g., behavioral approaches, medication-assisted treatment, mutual help groups) to help people recover and improve their lives.

Empathy and acceptance help us reduce the stigma people with substance use issues experience, reframe how people see themselves and their futures, create a safe space for exploring their goals and next steps, and increase long-term recovery outcomes (Miller, Forcehimes, & Zweben, 2019). Establishing agreement about whether and how to work together increases engagement, adherence, and long-term recovery (Bordin, 1979; Valle, 1981). To identify and address attitudes that may interfere with treatment adherence and long-term recovery, practitioners explore four basic areas:

- The nature and severity of the person's substance use and related consequences.
- Motivation for change.
- Personal strengths and resources.
- The role substance use plays in the person's life.

Attitudes about and reasons for using substances often create barriers to change that need to be addressed before the person's interest in abstaining or reducing use can emerge. Rapport, respect, and collaboration combined with empathic exploration of substance use and related issues form the basis for charting a path to change. Achieving long-term recovery from problematic substance use can take time and multiple attempts. Our ability to respond to a recurrence of substance use with empathy and acceptance helps to reduce stigma and increase willingness to reconsider change. Empathy and acceptance increase the person's openness to learning from the recurrence and to continuing working toward long-term recovery.

As we learn about the nature and severity of a person's substance use (i.e., what they have been using, how, how much, and how often) we ask open questions to communicate interest in the person's perspective, rather than to fact find or gather history. This interest in their point of view enhances the person's engagement and exploration of how their substance use helps them cope with difficult situations and how it makes them feel. We use reflections and summaries to show we understand the person's experience of how their substance use helps and how it impacts their health, mental health, and functioning in important roles (i.e., parent, employment, decision making).

Our ability to convey understanding and acceptance helps the person explore their perspective and experience more fully. Genuine affirmations of the person's efforts, intentions, strengths, and skills shift how the person sees themselves and cultivates hope and recovery capacity. Seeking collaboration and emphasizing autonomy reduce anxiety and discord and increase rapport.

Recurrence of substance use is common. After initiating harm reduction or abstinence, people may reexperience the reasons why they started using the substance in the first place (e.g., social anxiety, depression, panic attacks, PTSD), triggering a return to substance use. People are likely to see these bumps in the road as failures, which can lead to full recurrence of substance use and related problems.

MI processes and skills can be particularly useful during recurrence. MI practitioners normalize the experience as a learning opportunity, and express accurate empathy, acceptance, autonomy support, and collaboration to increase hope and shift the person's focus from shame ("something must be wrong with me") to even more effective plans for reinitiating abstinence and building coping skills. Helpful open questions that guide exploration of what happened and potential next steps include:

- "What happened right before you used *x*?"
- "How were you feeling?"
- "What other changes did you notice?"
- "What were you thinking before you used? What led you to being in a position to use?"
- "What did you do to avoid using? What else might have helped?"
- "After you used, what happened? How did you feel? What did you think?"
- "Where are you now in your thinking about quitting, cutting down, etc.?"
- "Looking ahead, where would you be in six months if you continued to use?"
- "What will your life be like in six months if you reinitiate your recovery now?"
- "What are some of your ideas for steps you can take to get back on your recovery journey?"

YOUR WORK WITH PEOPLE EXPERIENCING ISSUES WITH SUBSTANCE USE

· · · · · ·

What strategies are you already using in your work with people who experience issues with substance use?

_____

_____

_____

_____

_____

What has worked well for you?

_____

_____

_____

_____

_____

What supports (e.g., policies and procedures, supervision, MI training) does your organization offer for working with this population?

_____

_____

_____

_____

_____

THOUGHT DISORDERS

Many people who experience thought disorders live in isolation, distress, chaos, and fear. For many, this experience is compounded by involuntary treatment (e.g., involuntary commitment, involuntary medication orders). MI spirit and skills support the strong working alliance required to engage people who have these experiences into effective conversations about change. Genuine efforts to understand, collaborate, and help people reach their life goals shift the person's perception of themselves from feeling "like a diagnosis" to feeling "like a person who has the capacity to recover (Bjornestadt et al., 2019; Dobber, et al., 2018; Dobber et al., 2020, Topor, Bøe, & Larsen, 2017). When empathy and trust are established, people open up and talk freely about their experiences. This makes it possible for the person to make sense of their experiences, their perception of themselves, and their perception of the world. MI-consistent spirit and skills help us avoid superficial conversations that do *not* support the working alliance and momentum for change, such as (Bjornestadt et al., 2018; Dobber et al., 2018, 2020):

- Pretending to agree with a person's unusual beliefs.
- Focusing on exploring fixed beliefs.
- Asking too many questions.
- Following only the practitioner's agenda.
- Focusing on the facts of the person's situation instead of their *experience and perception* of the facts.
- Missing opportunities to elicit and strengthen change talk.

Normalizing, Affirming, and Looking Ahead

Normalizing, affirming and looking ahead are helpful approaches to engaging people who experience thought disorders. *Normalizing* the person's experience of distressing symptoms and expectation of recovery increases a person's hope for recovery and decreases their sense of shame and stigma. The following practitioner statements illustrate this strategy:

- "There are lots of different reasons why people hear voices that others can't hear. For example, after someone a person is close to dies, it is common to hear the person's voice. When people don't get enough sleep for a long time, it is common to hear people talking that other people can't hear."
- "People often find that it takes time to return to feeling like they are functioning at their usual levels again."
- "That experience of seeing and hearing things others don't can be a lot like dreaming—the experience seems so real and yet the experience is private, not public. Other people can't see or hear them."

Affirming the person's efforts to cope with difficult experiences (e.g., hearing critical voices) supports the person's interest in exploring other coping strategies. As the person strengthens their capacity for change, their hope, self-confidence, and interest in long-term changes increases. *Looking ahead* to anticipate distressing situations and explore practical ways to manage barriers to progress also increases the person's sense of safety, hope, and confidence. Practical strategies for coping with distressing situations include:

- ideas for responding to others' low expectations;
- establishing routines for eating and sleeping; and
- listening to music and exercising before sleep to cope with negative voices.

When the person's choices contribute to their own risk and vulnerability, it is helpful to develop a deeper understanding of the person's perspective and experience (i.e., strengthen the working alliance and trust) before working together to identify mutually acceptable healthier choices. Consider Ben:

Ben has a fixed belief that he owns the local university. This belief is a part of his rationale that he doesn't need an apartment. Homeless, on the street, Ben has repeatedly refused housing services, medication, and other efforts to engage him. Ben doesn't trust most people and doesn't want to go back to the hospital again. While talking with Ben, the ACT Team peer worker wonders whether Ben needs an office. Ben considers this option and eventually agrees. He moves into his "office"— an apartment with a desk. The ACT Team now meets regularly with Ben at his office and continues to engage him at his pace into services to support his recovery.

Accommodating Ben's challenges in coping with his symptoms increases his ability to participate in conversations about change. Compassionate understanding and autonomy support strengthen the person's sense of safety and responsibility for their own well-being.

Reflecting

People with thought disorders sometimes communicate through metaphorical or unusual speech or nonverbal behavior. Reflections can help the person clarify their meaning (i.e., "yes, that's it," "no,…") and strengthen the working alliance and engagement. For example:

Practitioner: "Tell me what you like about church."

Person: "It's Genesis inside, it's terrible not to see. I am blind." [Stands up, walks over to the light switch, and turns on the light.]

Practitioner: "You feel like church brings light into your life."

Person: "Yes. That's right." [Sits back down.]

Practitioner: "You want us to work on getting your meds sorted out so you can go back to church."

Person: "Yes."

Longer pauses following reflections and questions help the person process the information and track the conversation more easily. Consider this interaction with Jose:

Jose: "The brain clogins foul my thoughts…"

Practitioner: "It sounds like you are saying that the 'clogins' you feel in your brain are making it hard for you to express yourself."

Jose: "Yeah."

Practitioner: "When you mentioned your brother, I thought you looked a bit down. How might your brother be related to your recent troubles?" [long pause]

Jose: "He doesn't talk anymore."

Practitioner: "It sounds like he's important to you." [long pause]

Jose: [nods]

Practitioner: "And not talking with him makes it harder for you to see how you might cope." [long pause]

Jose: [nods]

Practitioner: "And so you decided to come here to find ways to get back on track with a job and make things right with your brother." [long pause]

Jose: [sighs]

Practitioner: "It sounds like I missed something there. Maybe it's not making things right with your brother. Maybe you want him to make things right with you."

Jose: "Yeah."

Practitioner: "What are you hoping he'll do?"

Jose: [Long silence, his head drops, he seems more upset.]

Practitioner: "It looks like this is hard for you. Like something is especially painful for you."

Jose: "[mumbling] … sleep."

Practitioner: "Okay, I can see you are tired."

Jose: "Uh-huh."

Early conversations focus on establishing safety, basic self-care routines, and managing distressing symptoms. As experiences of distress and chaos lessen, trust and hope increase, and it becomes possible to identify change goals that support recovery initiation.

YOUR WORK WITH PEOPLE EXPERIENCING SYMPTOMS OF THOUGHT DISORDER

· · · · · ·

What strategies are you already using in your work with people who experience symptoms of thought disorder?

_____

_____

_____

_____

_____

What has worked well for you?

_____

_____

_____

_____

What supports (e.g., policies and procedures, supervision, MI training) does your organization offer for working with this population?

_____

_____

_____

_____

_____

CHAPTER SUMMARY

• • • • • •

What do you see as the most important points of this chapter?

_____

_____

_____

_____

_____

What interested you the most?

_____

_____

_____

_____

_____

What information seemed most relevant to your practice?

_____

_____

_____

_____

_____

2

STRENGTHENING THE SPIRIT OF MOTIVATIONAL INTERVIEWING

The truth of a thing is in the feel of it, not in the think of it.
—Stanley Kubrick

IN THIS CHAPTER

- Components of MI Spirit
- Turning "What's Wrong" into "What's Strong"
- Strengthening MI Spirit and Avoiding Burnout with Mindful Practices
- Monitoring Your MI Spirit Over Time

The spirit of MI is a *mindset* and *heartset* that informs our conversations with others. It is the good soil that nourishes change, the background music without which the words are hollow. Early descriptions of MI focused on conversational skills and strategies that could help people change. Drs. Miller and Rollnick quickly discovered that to be effective, MI practitioners need to convey a particular MI spirit. Simply by wanting to help people change, we bring some of the heartset and mindset vital to an MI approach, and in some ways are already expressing MI spirit. In this chapter, we discuss ways to convey the spirit of MI.

COMPONENTS OF MI SPIRIT

The MI spirit can be described as having four distinct and synergistic components: partnership, compassion, acceptance, and evocation.

Partnership

Partnership is something we do *with* and *for* a person, rather than something we do *on* or *to* a person. Both people in the partnership are equal. Assuming and communicating that we have the best answers to a person's problems has been called the *expert trap*. The expert trap can assume a variety of guises:

- Asking a barrage of questions to collect information with the intention of providing an answer or solution for the person's challenges.
- Saying "Just do this," "Don't do that," or "Why don't you try that?"
- Providing solutions and suggestions without first asking for the person's ideas or asking permission to consider additional ideas together.
- Otherwise holding ourselves out as the expert on why and how the person should change.

Reactance is an unpleasant motivational reaction when a person perceives that someone or something is threatening their behavioral choices or limiting their range of alternatives.

We can see that entering the conversation—or taking over—as the expert is, in many respects, inconsistent with the MI spirit. When we fall into the expert trap, we can create reactance within the person, cause interpersonal discord, demonstrate a lack of respect for the person's insights and resources, and/or put the person into a passive role for their own change process (Brehm & Brehm, 1981).

It can be particularly difficult to stay within the MI spirit when the conversation feels like it is not going well, or we feel concern about a person's choices. Think about a recent change conversation that felt tense, edgy, or tight in some way. When conversations are not going smoothly, it is natural to feel as if we or the other person should have acted differently. This tense feeling may be accompanied by a sense of ourselves as being right or somehow feeling uncertain, unable, smaller, or more vulnerable. When we are in this tense mindset, it is natural to use an expert stance, ask more questions, and engage in behaviors that are not consistent with the spirit of MI.

This self-reflection exercise helps you move from a tense expert stance to an open, relaxed, and curious stance that is consistent with the spirit of MI. Some MI practitioners find it helpful to keep exercises like this somewhere close so that they can review them when needed. Regular, even daily, self-reflection on our practice increases our ability to recognize opportunities to shift into an even more effective MI practice.

AVOIDING THE EXPERT TRAP

• • • • • •

We all fall into the expert trap from time to time. Describe a situation where you approached a conversation from the expert role.

_____

_____

_____

_____

_____

How did the person respond to you?

_____

_____

_____

_____

What assumptions were you making about your responsibility for the person's change? What happened in the conversation—was there something specific that might have sprung the expert trap? Something the person said? A concern you had? Certain personal values?

_____

_____

_____

_____

Hold and appreciate your values and intentions and resist the temptation to judge yourself for not being flawless. What are your "best self" strengths and intentions that you express in your concerns and values?

_____

_____

_____

_____

_____

As you learned more about the person's ideas, insights, and resources, how did they surprise or delight you, or give you a sense of optimism that the person was capable of resolving their own concerns?

_____

_____

_____

_____

_____

Rewrite the relevant part of the conversation. How could you use your intentions, values, strengths, and MI spirit to approach the conversation from a partnering perspective?

_____

_____

_____

_____

_____

When we convey a sense of *partnership* in our conversations, we work with a person collaboratively to form and sustain an alliance. We value the person's ideas and expertise. Our ideas and expertise are helpful only if the person thinks they are and feels able to use our contribution to move toward their goals. We tailor information to the person's interests and collaborate with them to identify ideas for moving forward:

- "I'd like to be helpful here, and you can let me know what would work for you."
- "How would you see us working together on this?"
- "I can tell you about some options others have found helpful in similar situations, if you'd like.

Compassion

Compassion is the understanding of another's pain and the desire to somehow ease that pain. When we convey a sense of compassion, we are alongside the person in their experience as they work to resolve their challenges, suffering, and difficulties.

Demonstrating compassion means deliberately committing to and actively promoting the other person's welfare; it is giving priority to their needs. When we find ourselves thinking that we don't "like" how someone is behaving, we can pause and ask ourselves how they are hurting. This moment of reflection helps us shift from a place of judgment to one of openhearted compassion.

PRACTICING COMPASSION

• • • • • •

Think of someone you know who is having a hard time. Perhaps they are feeling depressed, anxious, afraid, or like a failure. Imagine yourself asking, "Where does it hurt?" and "What is it like for you?" You might imagine leaning toward them, your heart reaching out to them.

What do you think the person would most need to hear or want from you right now?

_____

_____

_____

_____

_____

What is your sense of yourself when you are practicing compassion?

_____

_____

_____

_____

_____

Perspective and Compassion

What happens when we are frustrated with another's choices or lack of action? What effect does that feeling of urgency, frustration, anger, or blame have on our effectiveness? What is the impact of looking at a situation from a different perspective? Consider this story:

> *Ruby is diagnosed with a serious and chronic mental health issue. She is living with her partner and young child. Although they have a place to live, Ruby is barely managing to stretch her income to pay the rent and bills. They are on the cusp of homelessness.*

She tells you that her partner is the source of her pain and struggle. Her partner spends their time playing video games and does not contribute to the household upkeep and expenses. Ruby is often moved to tears as she expresses her frustration. Recently, the partner asked Ruby to move into a new subsidized apartment with them, but there is a catch. The partner would have to be the only identified renter because if Ruby were also on the lease, the apartment would be too expensive. Ruby has two months to decide whether to stay in her current apartment (with her child and without her partner) or for both of them to move in with her partner.

PERSPECTIVE AND COMPASSION

• • • • • •

As you consider Ruby's suffering and her dilemma, how do you feel?

_____

_____

_____

What do you think she should do?

_____

_____

_____

Many practitioners would find Ruby's struggle to be understandable but also a bit frustrating. The belief tends to be that Ruby lacks the confidence to live on her own, and if she could increase her self-confidence, then it would resolve her dilemma. However, all efforts to boost her self-confidence (e.g., affirming all of her hard work in maintaining the apartment, paying the bills on her own, taking care of her child, etc.) appear to do nothing to help.

You remember that Ruby once told you that she grew up in foster care and that her experience was traumatic. How does that information shift your perspective and help you to understand and resonate with her dilemma?

_____

_____

_____

What might her dilemma actually be?

_____

_____

_____

What could you say to her to capture what you believe the dilemma may be?

_____

_____

_____

How can you phrase it to help her more easily resolve her dilemma?

_____

_____

_____

How do you think she might respond to a statement like this: "You've been working really hard to hold this family together. It's important to you that your child's experience growing up isn't like yours. You want her to know that she is loved by two parents and that she has a stable home."

_____

_____

_____

Write out what you think she might say in response.

_____

_____

_____

Describe how you might work together with Ruby to reframe her dilemma in a way that helps her envision her options for keeping herself and her child safe, healthy, and stably housed.

_____

_____

_____

_____

_____

_____

_____

Increasing Compassion for Others Through Self-Acceptance and Self-Compassion

When we find ourselves in the expert trap, feeling frustrated, focusing on the person's struggles and limitations instead of their strengths and resources, we want to shift into working within the MI spirit. A strong self-compassion practice increases our ability to make this shift. Self-compassion helps us:

- Respond to personal mistakes, failures, and inadequacies with kindness rather than harsh self-judgment.
- Accept our imperfections as part of the shared human experience; we are *all* fallible.
- Attend to our experience with acceptance instead of pushing it away.

You will find tools for building self-compassion and self-acceptance later in this chapter.

Acceptance

Practicing acceptance (sometimes called "the four A's") means:

- Affirming the person.
- Acknowledging and prizing their absolute worth.
- Expressing accurate empathy.
- Supporting their autonomy.

In conveying acceptance, we explicitly affirm the person's strengths, skills, efforts, and capacities. We acknowledge and value the person's worth *as they are* and as they are changing, rather than requiring them to earn worth or justify their value. We demonstrate understanding of the person's perspective—without judgment—through the quality of our listening and our ability to reflect that we hear what is said, as well as what is meant. We convey the desire to help the person expand their sense of choice and control, weigh their options, and activate their own expertise for choices that are consistent with their values and strengths. We support and respect the person's ability and right to choose their own path: "You really know yourself and your situation best, and I'm wondering what you think would be some good options for you going forward."

Showing acceptance doesn't mean that we agree with the person's perspective or approve of a particular situation. Accepting a person, or "what is," means setting our judgments—positive and negative—aside. Accepting the person, or the situation, allows the person to relax. No defense is needed, and the person is more likely to self-explore with us. It gives them space to begin thinking about making changes that are consistent with their values and strengths.

APPRECIATING STRENGTHS— IT STARTS WITH US

· · · · · ·

It can be useful—even before looking for the strengths in the people with whom we work—to identify the strengths and capacities that *we* bring to our work. Are you caring? Compassionate? A good listener? Curious? Optimistic? Delighted by the resourcefulness of the people with whom you work?

What strengths do you bring to your work? How do they help you convey the spirit of MI?

_____

_____

_____

_____

_____

_____

_____

_____

_____

TUNING IN TO APPRECIATION

· · · · · ·

We often tend to habitually scan for what's wrong. It helps to *practice* seeing and sharing a person's strengths.

Imagine the person you thought about during the *Practicing Compassion* exercise. Think about why you really care about them. Imagine what they are like when they are happy. Imagine what they are like when they are at their best.

How would you describe the person's best self? As you see their best self, pay attention to how it feels to recognize this part of them.

_____

_____

_____

_____

Imagine sharing with the person the "best self" characteristics you see in them. How might they feel and how might they respond to your description of their best self?

_____

_____

_____

_____

Genuinely affirming others taps into our own strengths and sense of well-being. How do *you* feel and what is your sense of yourself when you are seeing the best in others?

_____

_____

_____

_____

Evocation

Evocation in MI is very much strength-based: We assume that the person already has most of what they need, and we help them find it by exploring their priorities, concerns, strengths, resources, wisdom, and good ideas for change. This approach is the opposite of the deficit assumption, in which the person is viewed as lacking the necessary insight and resources for their own change and that it is our job to supply it. The deficit assumption is inconsistent with an MI approach and can lead to problematic outcomes.

People change because they change their own perspective about making a change, not because we change their perspective for them. We support this shift by expressing interest and curiosity about the person's point of view:

- "I'm eager to hear your ideas for approaching this."
- "How will you know when you are ready?"
- "How would this change make your life better? What else?"
- "What are some options you want to try to get started? What ideas do you have?"

Ultimately, people make their own decisions about what they will do and how they will do it. When we take responsibility for the person's change—because we believe that we really know what's best for them—we risk:

- Burning ourselves out because we don't control the outcome.
- Creating interpersonal discord.
- Complicating the person's own change process.

TURNING "WHAT'S WRONG" INTO "WHAT'S STRONG"

Our ability to convey MI spirit derives at least in part from cultivating and holding the belief that people already have inside them the capacity and potential for change. One way that this belief manifests is through an ongoing "treasure hunt" for a person's skills, strengths, capacities, and efforts. We can run aground when we search for "what's wrong" in a situation or see the person as "ineffective." With a shift in perspective, we can instead discover "what's strong." Consider this case example:

A group of detention officers in a juvenile justice center were perplexed about a 17-year-old woman, Tanya, held there. They talked together in a team meeting with some outside practitioners about how she had, on three occasions, nearly completed her mandated month's stay, only to engage in some small infraction that extended her time. "She's going to be 18 on the day now set for her release. Can you believe it?" one said to another. "She seems smart, but how dumb can you be? She's so impulsive and doesn't understand the rules here; just no insight at all. One month is now going to be 10 months by the time she gets out of here. What a waste!"

A consulting mental health practitioner looked at this situation differently. From her perspective, working with exploited youth, Tanya's actions made perfect sense. At the time of her arrest, Tanya had been in a department store with the man who was exploiting her. She took a big step away from him, grabbed a package of socks, waved it in front of the security camera, and then concealed the

package in her coat. Being taken into custody and charged with shoplifting
separated her from this man, and rather than be released to him, she extended her stay at the
detention center so that she could be released as an adult on her 18th birthday. "In my opinion, she
is clever, insightful, knowledgeable, and resourceful," said the practitioner. "Adding time to her stay
was the best way for her to maintain her current, relative safety until her release as an adult."

If you have trouble seeing Tanya's shoplifting from a strengths-based perspective, as the detention officers did, you are not alone. This deficit perspective is typical of how some of us were raised. Often, we begin to embrace and develop a strengths-based perspective for the first time when we start practicing MI.

TURNING "WHAT'S WRONG" INTO "WHAT'S STRONG"

· · · · · ·

Describe a time when you focused on what didn't seem to be going well in a person's life or what you thought they were doing "wrong" in a situation.

_____

_____

_____

_____

What might be an alternative way to look at it? What different perspective might the person have had in the situation? What are the person's decisions or qualities that looked like mistakes or deficits but could really be strengths or insights? Describe this alternative in as much detail as you can.

_____

_____

_____

_____

STRENGTHENING MI SPIRIT AND AVOIDING BURNOUT WITH MINDFUL PRACTICES

In order to strengthen our ability to sustain the MI spirit, we can use daily practices involving mindful breathing, self-compassion, patience, generosity, and forgiveness. These sorts of practices also help us avoid burnout in our professional work. You may already have favorite mindful practices that work well for you. Next are some practices that we use to sustain MI spirit in our work.

> *Mindfulness means paying attention in a particular way: on purpose, in the present moment, and nonjudgmentally.*
>
> —Jon Kabat-Zinn

Mindful Breathing

Mindful breathing can help us strengthen our self-compassion and our ability to convey the MI spirit. Mindful breathing—slow, deep, and focused—calms the body and mind by stimulating the vagus nerve that manages the parasympathetic nervous system. The breath lowers stress, reduces heart rate, and lowers blood pressure. It calms us down.

Attention on our breath grounds us more in the present moment. When we are in the present, we stop focusing on our regrets about the past, worries about the future, and our own self-judgments. It gives us a break from repetitive and relentless stress and allows the body and mind a moment for rest and recovery. Calmness can help us see ourselves, others, and situations more clearly, and bring increased acceptance and compassion to ourselves and others. It allows us to bring curiosity and interest—rather than frustration and impatience—into our encounters.

MINDFUL BREATHING

· · · · · ·

Thich Nhat Hanh (2014) describes a simple practice of mindfully noticing the breath to bring our awareness into the present moment:

- On an inbreath, say to yourself, "I am breathing in."

- On the outbreath, say to yourself, "I am breathing out."

- Continue breathing in this manner for however long you like.

Notice what happens as you try this practice:

- Notice how your breath changes as you pay attention to it, how it becomes longer and slower.

- Notice how your thoughts slow down.

- Notice how you might feel more peace or space to observe your thoughts and feelings.

- Notice your mind wandering. This will definitely happen! Simply bring your attention back to the breath with self-compassion.

Even simpler is the practice of one mindful breath. One mindful breath—six seconds maximum—can be surprisingly effective. Taking one mindful breath before each clinical encounter or work meeting is a convenient and self-determining way to recharge our systems.

SELF-COMPASSION BREAK

• • • • • •

Think of a current life or work struggle that is causing you distress. Place one or both hands over your heart. While still holding the struggle in mind, say to yourself:

- "This is a moment of suffering."

- "Suffering is part of life."

- "May I be kind to myself in this moment."

- "May I give myself the compassion I need."

(Modified from Neff & Dahm, 2015)

Loving-Kindness Meditation

How can we build our openness to what is unspoken in others' hearts (e.g., the wish for a "real family," the feeling of not being good enough, the feeling that the situation is unfair)? Loving-kindness meditations are designed to intentionally cultivate compassion for ourselves and others (Hofmann, Grossman, & Hinton, 2011). Loving-kindness meditations (also called *metta*) incorporate physical self-soothing actions into the meditation, like placing our hands over our hearts, especially in times of stress. A regular loving-kindness meditation practice helps to build resilient compassion for ourselves and others. These are two guided loving-kindness meditations that you can try; there are many more available online:

- https://jackkornfield.com/meditation-lovingkindness/
- https://www.youtube.com/watch?v=sz7cpV7ERsM

Forgiveness Meditation

Forgiveness meditation offers a way to uncover pain and beliefs that have blocked forgiveness and help us let go of past hurts. It also uncovers blocked forgiveness for ourselves when we have hurt others through our own fear, anger, and confusion. This meditation brings about forgiveness in the spirit of loving-kindness without necessitating shame. Forgiveness meditation does not condone harmful actions, and it does not compel us to right any wrongs. But it does help us restore our hearts to full capacity for love. These guided forgiveness meditations are available online:

- http://www.compassion-training.org/en/media/player.php?id=a14
- https://www.tarabrach.com/guided-forgiveness-meditation

Breathing Compassion In and Out

Compassion involves resonating with another's suffering, experiencing it deeply, and putting ourselves in another's shoes. How can we be alongside people who are suffering without becoming overwhelmed by the suffering and burning out? Our instinctive response to emotional discomfort is to push it away, sometimes by engaging in the expert trap. Responding to suffering in this way leads to more suffering for both people in the conversation and can potentially lead to practitioner burnout.

We lessen our own suffering by being attuned to it with kind acceptance. Similarly, we can lessen others' suffering by listening deeply *with the purpose of giving them a chance to suffer less*. Rather than taking responsibility for fixing their pain, we open up opportunities for them to discover how they can achieve their goals through making different choices.

Practitioners can manage the discomfort of being present with another's suffering by slightly adapting the exercise from the Mindful Breathing tool described earlier. Instead of following the breath to increase awareness of the present:

- Breathe in the person's pain and suffering with the inbreath.
- Breathe out kindness and compassion with the outbreath.

Or

- Breathe in compassion for ourselves on the inbreath.
- Breathe out compassion for the person with whom we're working on the outbreath.

Gratitude Practices

Another way to strengthen compassion, reduce the potential for burnout, and increase resilience and happiness is to increase our experience of gratitude and kindness in the world. Gratitude, especially as a daily practice, creates a positive lens for viewing the world. This lens can protect us from becoming overwhelmed by negative experiences. Here's how it works (Emmons & Mishra, 2012):

- Someone does something for you, a kind act, and it increases your sense of self-worth. Because this person thinks highly enough of you to go out of their way to be generous to you, you must be worth it.
- You thank them for their kind act. By recognizing their kindness, you increase your sense of social connection in the world (as opposed to behaving as if you are entitled to the kind acts received).
- The act of expressing gratitude sets off a chain reaction where you continue to experience gratitude, joy, wonder, and connection through increased openness to these experiences in your daily existence.

Daily gratitude practices support our ability to experience connection, kindness, and compassion even in the face of stress, overwhelm, and loss. As a bonus, these practices can result in higher levels of enthusiasm, determination, attentiveness, and energy (Emmons & McCullough, 2003). A simple daily gratitude practice involves keeping a journal of three things we feel grateful for every day or having a gratitude accountability partner and sending each other a daily text or email with the three things for which we feel grateful that day. For more information on daily gratitude practices, check out the following resources:

- Four Great Gratitude Strategies: http://greatergood.berkeley.edu/article/item/four_great_gratitude_strategies
- Ten Ways to Become More Grateful: http://greatergood.berkeley.edu/article/item/ten_ways_to_become_more_grateful1/

MONITORING YOUR MI SPIRIT OVER TIME

Chapter 10 discusses specific ways in which you can maintain and deepen your MI practice over time. For now, though, these exercises can help you stay attuned to the MI spirit specifically.

EAVESDROPPING

• • • • • •

Your last scheduled session of the day has just ended, and the person is waiting outside the building for a lift from a friend. As you leave the building, you pass by this person—who is talking on their cell phone to someone—and you realize that they are talking about the session. What are they saying about you and their experience? For example: "My counselor really listens to me, she believes in me, and respects my opinion. She works with me to help me figure out what I want to do." Or is it something less positive? Get as specific and detailed as you can, using words and phrases the person would be using.

_____

_____

_____

_____

_____

_____

_____

_____

_____

_____

_____

MIRROR, MIRROR ON THE WALL...

• •

This activity is intended to help you monitor and strengthen your ability to stay within the spirit of MI. For this exercise, find a friend or colleague who is willing to have a brief conversation about a change that they are considering, either personally or professionally. The change under consideration should be something that is real, has some meaning for them, and is something they feel comfortable talking about with you. It doesn't have to be a long conversation—up to 10 minutes is sufficient.

At the end of the 10 minutes, please thank your friend or colleague for talking with you and invite them to join you in assessing your use of the MI spirit by rating each of the six statements below, then sharing your responses with one another. *Include specific examples that support your ratings*. Use this exercise as an opportunity to identify what you are doing well and what you might do differently to convey the MI spirit more effectively. If you are both learning about and practicing MI, you can change roles and repeat the exercise. You will need to make two copies of these pages for this exercise. You may want to make more copies so that you can repeat the exercise occasionally.

Scale

1	2	3	4	5

Not at All   Moderately   Very Much

Friend or Colleague	Practitioner
_____ "I felt respected by the practitioner."	_____ "I showed respect for my friend or colleague." [Absolute Worth]
_____ "I felt heard and understood."	_____ "I listened and demonstrated understanding." [Empathy]
_____ "I felt I could trust the practitioner."	_____ "I showed my friend or colleague that they could trust me." [Compassion]
_____ "The practitioner asked about my ideas for my own change."	_____ "I showed interest and curiosity about their ideas for change." [Evocation]
_____ "I feel we worked well together in the conversation."	_____ "We worked well together in the conversation." [Partnership]
_____ "The practitioner supported my ability to make choices for myself."	_____ "I supported my friend/colleague's ability to make their own choices." [Autonomy Support]

REMEMBERING A STORY
OF THE MI SPIRIT

• • • • • •

You have probably conveyed the spirit of MI, or aspects of it, in your change conversations; or perhaps you experienced MI spirit in a change conversation you had with another person.

Write a brief description of that experience, what we call a "spirit story." What allowed you or the other person to provide an experience that was in the spirit of MI? What was the impact of that experience?

_____

_____

_____

_____

_____

_____

_____

_____

_____

_____

_____

_____

EXPRESSING THE SPIRIT OF MI

• • • • • •

Watch either or both of these video examples:

- Empathy: The Human Connection to Patient Care

  https://www.youtube.com/watch?v=cDDWvj_q-o8

- Under the Surface

  https://www.youtube.com/watch?v=AZ-pU7ozt3g

How would you express the MI spirit so that you could stand alongside any of the people in these clips and really understand them? How would you create an atmosphere of acceptance and compassion so that what is under the surface rises to the level of conversation and mutual understanding? Be as specific as you can in your descriptions.

_____

_____

_____

_____

_____

_____

_____

_____

_____

We hope that this chapter has given you some ideas for strengthening the spirit of MI in your work. We also hope that as you try some of these mindful exercises you experience even more happiness and resilience in your own lives.

CHAPTER SUMMARY

· · · · · ·

What do you see as the most important points of this chapter?

_____

_____

_____

_____

What new insight did you gain?

_____

_____

_____

_____

What are you most likely to try in your practice this week? For your own self-care?

_____

_____

_____

_____

3

CONVERSATIONS ABOUT CHANGE

People are generally better persuaded by the reasons which they have themselves discovered than by those which have come into the mind of others.

—Blaise Pascal

IN THIS CHAPTER

- Constructive Conversations About Change

- Interpersonal Communication Styles and Conversations About Change

- Ambivalence About Change

- Components of an Effective Motivational Conversation 1: MI-Consistent Behaviors, MI-Inconsistent Behaviors, Evocative Behaviors

- Components of an Effective Motivational Conversation 2: Relational and Technical Components

- Brief Conversations About Change

- Introducing MI Processes and Core Skills

CONSTRUCTIVE CONVERSATIONS ABOUT CHANGE

MI is a way to have constructive conversations about change. The greater the role a behavior plays in a person's life, the more difficult it can be to change. Consider a young man, diagnosed with bipolar disorder and cannabis use disorder, who chooses to smoke marijuana instead of taking prescription medications. Sometimes, his choices lead him to strike out at his mom, with whom he lives and wants to have a good relationship. Many factors impact the practitioner's ability to engage the young man in a conversation about change:

- Developing trust and addressing the feelings that naturally occur when someone considers change, such as fear, shame, pride, and self-doubt.

- Developing an understanding of the young man's perspective of the situation and listening to his ideas for goals and his ideas for making a change.
- Engaging the young man's many strengths, good ideas, and resources to ensure his success.
- Balancing the practitioner's concerns about their own ability to guide the conversation toward change with their responsibility to attend to both the young man's and his mother's well-being.

There are many paths that this conversation may take that support the young man in reaching the goals that are most important to him. A common challenge to productive conversations about change is that we are often expected to focus on certain high-priority changes (e.g., medication adherence, reducing substance use, developing coping skills, getting a job), but people often have good reasons to avoid these changes (e.g., intense anxiety, firmly established ways of coping in difficult situations, fear, self-doubt, pride). It's not surprising when conversations that are supposed to be about change end up sounding like the practitioner on one side, trying to get the person to do something, and the person on the other side with a different, even diametrically opposed, goal for change. Consider the following brief exchanges where the practitioner and person seem to be at odds:

Sam wants a girlfriend, but his outpatient clinician has been told that the priority needs to be to get him to adhere to medications for his bipolar disorder:

Sam: "You said we could work on my goals. I want a girlfriend."

Practitioner: "Yes, we're going to work on your goals. But first, you need to take your meds. Remember what happened the last time you stopped taking them? Do you want that to happen again?"

Evelyn wants an apartment and wants to be reunited with her grown children, but the outreach team is told she needs to be sober first and she needs to be treated for breast cancer. She's refusing all treatment, and her children are refusing to see her:

Evelyn: "I don't need treatment; I need my own apartment where my kids can visit me."

Practitioner: "Every time we get you an apartment you end up getting drunk and trashing it. Let's try something different this time. Let's talk about treatment programs and looking after your health."

Joe has chronic pain that is managed through medication, but he believes he would be more comfortable if he could also smoke weed. He knows if he smokes weed that his doctors will take away the pain medication. The counselor is expected to help him quit smoking weed and cigarettes.

Joe: "I'm still in pain all the time. The meds help but weed would help more. I just can't risk the urine screen—they'll take away the meds, and then I'll really be stuck."

Practitioner: "You want to smoke weed, and you know your cigarette smoking is already endangering your health. Let's talk about how you could quit smoking and then we can talk about other ways to manage your pain."

It's common in these types of situations to feel mystified about how to guide a conversation about change with someone who seems disinterested, disengaged, angry, or just plain stuck. The concern that practitioners have for the people they serve, in combination with the external expectation that we bring about difficult changes, often produce communication styles that are unhelpful, such as asking many fact-finding questions, giving directive advice, persuading, or confronting. Such communication styles reduce the likelihood that a person will be willing to engage in services and make conversations about meaningful changes even less likely.

INTERPERSONAL COMMUNICATION STYLES AND CONVERSATIONS ABOUT CHANGE

We can think of interpersonal communication styles as falling along a continuum, with *directing* and *following* at each end, and *guiding* as a middle approach (see Figure 1).

Directing	Guiding	Following
Telling	Collaborating	Allowing
Advising	Evoking	Permitting
Ordering	Increasing intrinsic motivation	Observing
Leading	Honoring Autonomy	Going along with

Figure 1. Interpersonal Communication Styles: A Continuum

We might describe a *directing* style as one in which the practitioner manages, advises, orders, decides, determines, and controls the goals and the process—perhaps even the very conversation itself. Sometimes the directing style is helpful. When there's an emergency or crisis (e.g., a fire alarm going off in the building), a directing style is certainly indicated. But difficulties can arise when practitioners are tempted to use a directing style in conversations about change: "If I just tell the person what to do and how to do it, then they will change, and their problems will go away." Some underlying assumptions here may be that the person doesn't know what to do, doesn't have their own ideas about change, and will become ready, willing, and able to change once they are given the solution. Often, our well-intentioned and knowledgeable advice doesn't lead to change—and it may very well push the person away from engaging with us. The previous three sample vignettes about Sam, Evelyn, and Joe are all examples of "directing."

At the other end of the spectrum is the *following* style, in which the practitioner allows, observes, or goes along with the person or follows along wherever the person is headed. We can imagine this style as being especially useful in scenarios where the person has already chosen a helpful path for change and not much input or additional support is needed. The practitioner might also adopt a following style earlier in the change process to be sure that they understand the person's dilemma or point of view, which serves as a prelude for the work they will do together.

A following style is *not* indicated and may even be counterproductive when a person is ready to set a target for change, begins thinking actively about change, or begins planning for change. For example, using our earlier scenarios, a following style offers only an echo of what the person wants without an invitation to explore the person's goals and values and how specific changes might be related to their goals and values:

> **Sam:** "You said we could work on my goals. I want a girlfriend."
>
> **Practitioner:** "You want a girlfriend."
>
> **Evelyn:** "I don't need treatment; I need my own apartment where my kids can visit me."
>
> **Practitioner:** "You want your kids to visit you."
>
> **Joe:** "I'm still in pain all the time. The meds help but weed would help more. I just can't risk the urine screen—they'll take away the meds, and then I'll really be stuck."
>
> **Practitioner:** "You want to be able to smoke weed and take the meds."

A *guiding* style can be thought of as accompanying, collaborating, eliciting, shaping, and assisting the person in reaching their goals. MI is most accurately considered a refined form of guiding, where the practitioner partners with the person on change topics and pathways to change that are mutually acceptable within the *working alliance*. An apt metaphor for the guiding style is to view the practitioner as a tour guide (Miller & Rollnick, 2013). The tour guide finds out how the person sees things, what the person would like to see, and how the person sees the practitioner as helpful in getting them to their destination. Although the practitioner might offer a variety of paths for the person to consider, it is ultimately the person's choice to decide what works best for them, their reasons for going in that direction, and how they choose to get there. This approach brings forth the person's own *intrinsic motivation* to change. Returning to our earlier examples:

> **Sam:** "You said we could work on my goals. I want a girlfriend."
>
> **Practitioner:** "It's important to you to have someone special in your life, and you want to talk about how you might make that happen. And then, if you are willing, I'm interested in hearing your thoughts about how managing your mood even better than you are now might be a helpful part of your future success with that goal."
>
> **Evelyn:** "I don't need treatment; I need my own apartment where my kids can visit me."
>
> **Practitioner:** "You value the time you get to spend with your kids, and an apartment is a part of the plan that makes that possible. I wonder if we could talk about what might help you to maintain your next apartment so you have a stable place where the kids can visit you?"
>
> **Joe:** "I'm still in pain all the time. The meds help but weed would help more. I just can't risk the urine screen—they'll take away the meds, and then I'll really be stuck."
>
> **Practitioner:** "The pain is constant, and you are interested in your options for managing pain in a way that gives you a bit more freedom. One thing that you know has worked in the past is weed. What do you know about other options for managing your pain?"

The following exercises are intended to help you differentiate between the directing, following, and guiding styles, and help you brainstorm ways in which you can better integrate the guiding style into your practice.

EXPLORING THE CONTINUUM

· · · · · ·

Part 1: Directing

Step 1: Find a peer or friend willing to have a brief conversation about a change they are considering. Review together the description of "directing."

Step 2: Try a directing style of conversation with your peer or friend for up to 5 minutes.

Step 3: Pause and talk with each other about what happened in the conversation, what impact you had on their ideas, and their willingness and confidence for change.

Step 4: Switch roles and debrief again.

What did you notice about your experience on both sides of the directing conversation?

_____

_____

_____

_____

Part 2: Following

Now review the description of "following." Try the conversation again with a following style, switch roles, and debrief similarly. What did you notice about your experience on both sides of the following conversation?

_____

_____

_____

_____

_____

Part 3: Guiding

Now review the description of "guiding." This time try a more guiding style, switch roles, and debrief similarly. What did you notice about your experience on both sides of the guiding conversation?

_____

_____

_____

_____

_____

EXPLORING PERSONAL STYLE ON THE CONTINUUM

• • • • • •

Using the continuum concept (with directing at one end, following at the other, and guiding in the middle), evaluate the most recent conversation you had with a person you are serving. How would you characterize the style you used?

_____

_____

_____

_____

_____

If your style was not primarily guiding, how might you talk differently with that person the next time you see them to get closer to a guiding style?

_____

_____

_____

_____

_____

CREATE A GUIDING STYLE REMINDER

· · · · · ·

What sorts of visual cues or other reminders would be helpful in reminding you to start and stay in a guiding style during a conversation? For example, you might place a sticky note on your desk to remind you to incorporate a concept or strategy, like:

- Consider the person's perspective—what is most important to them!

- Explore values!

- Affirm strengths!

Or something to remind you *not* to do something, like:

- "No advice without permission" to support collaboration.

- "It's their choice" to support autonomy.

- "Values" and "strengths" to remember to evoke these.

What sort of reminders might be most helpful for *you*?

_____

_____

_____

_____

_____

In what form would the reminder work best as a conversation aid (e.g., sticky note, index card, list)?

_____

_____

_____

_____

_____

Create several guiding style reminders based on your answers. Once you have created your reminders, try them in your next session. After the session, answer the following questions about each reminder:

Did I use all the reminders? _____

In what ways were they useful?

_____

_____

_____

_____

_____

Are there ways I could tweak them so that they would be *more* useful?

_____

_____

_____

_____

_____

AMBIVALENCE ABOUT CHANGE

Ambivalence is a natural part of the change process; it represents a potentially helpful place of discovery and self-exploration. People often feel at least two ways about change—they want to maintain the status quo, and they also want to move toward change—and this ambivalence can manifest in many forms. At its simplest, we can imagine two big rubber bands: one that is holding a person where they are now and one that is pulling them to where they might go.

We can also think of ambivalence as two inner voices simultaneously competing with one another: one is reluctant about change, and the other is interested in change. At its core, ambivalence involves experiencing an attachment to, as well as a disenchantment with, the familiar. It is a wish to be somewhere else accompanied by apprehension about the journey or destination. A person's ambivalence about change often relates to *importance*:

- Where does this change rate in my priorities?
- How urgent is it for me?
- Why might I make a change?
- What do important people in my life think?
- What impact would it have for me to make this change?

Ambivalence also relates to *confidence*:

- Could I?
- What other difficult things have I done that would help me have confidence here?
- How could I overcome difficulties if I ran into them along the way?

The Righting Reflex

As practitioners, we have a natural desire to want to "fix" things or make things better for those we serve. Therefore, when we hear a person's reluctance, it is tempting to try and:

- Convince the person that they have a problem.
- Persuade them of the importance of the change ("You need to do this because…," "Negative things will happen if you don't…," "It's really important for you to do this").
- Cheerlead them into confidence ("I know you can…").
- Provide a solution for the problem ("It's really easy, you just need to…," "Well, why don't you try…," "You should just…").

We call these efforts—even when well-intentioned—the *righting reflex*: Trying to fix, solve, set right, or prevent the person from travelling a painful road by identifying a road we think is easier or more direct. What do you notice happens when we meet the person's ambivalence with our righting reflex? Typically, when we provide solutions, the person voices challenges. When we argue *for* change, the person's natural tendency is to argue *against* that change. That might sound like "Yes, but…," and what follows the "but" is usually talk against the very change the person might be considering. Despite our intention to "help," the righting reflex actually strengthens the rubber band that is holding the person where they are now. It may also rupture the person's willingness to work with us toward change (see Figure 2).

Figure 2: Ambivalence About Change

An important element of developing proficiency in MI is identifying where in the practitioner's style the righting reflex emerges and mindfully practicing MI-consistent skills to guide conversations about change.

Practitioners commonly experience frustration when people act as if any change under consideration is the practitioner's responsibility and not their own. We face this challenge most frequently when we experience deep concern for the well-being, safety, or choices of the people we serve. This concern activates our righting reflex and causes us, with the best of intentions, to:

- Forget that people have expertise in their own lives and assume we're the only expert in the room.

- Forget to ask for the person's ideas before asking permission to offer our own.

- Default to only asking questions or prioritizing fact-finding before understanding the person's perspective.

- Approach conversations with an undisclosed secondary agenda.

- Dwell only on barriers, challenges, or limitations.

- Use only a narrow range of evocative strategies when exploring importance, confidence, and readiness for change.

- Become frustrated with the person's goals or think that they should want something larger or something different.

We may be particularly vulnerable to the righting reflex when working with youth. Young people are often underestimated. It can be tempting to take the expert stance or try to voice the arguments for change.

Working with Ambivalence

While these challenges are common in mental health services, being proficient in MI helps practitioners navigate these concerns and conversations. MI proficiency supports our ability to use the skills and strategies of MI to enhance a person's exploration and discovery of their own good ideas for change. For example, reframing a person's behavior as a part of their ambivalence about change helps us better understand the person's perception of the situation and respond in ways that embody the spirit of MI. We might first take note of our *own* experience of concern and then be better able to understand the person's experience of lack of control over their own distress (e.g., "You want this to change. You feel like you would have changed it already if you had a way to do it that was in your control.").

Next, we might consider whether the person needs to access their own strengths, skills, and resources before attempting to focus on a specific change. One way we do this in MI is to ask, "Tell me what you're already doing." This gives us an opportunity to appreciate and affirm their current or recent efforts. We might also ask about their experience in the past when making a difficult change: "Tell me about a time in the past when you had to make a change. What did you do?" We might reflect the strengths and skills they used and ask about how they might use those strengths and skills to address their current situation. While this may not *resolve* the person's reluctance to change, it does give us the opportunity to understand a bit more about their situation and bring forward their strengths, skills, and own ideas about what might make sense for next steps.

Working with ambivalence is like those two big rubber bands: If our righting reflex pulls on the band tied to where they want to go, then the other band tightens, holding them where they are. The more our righting reflex pulls, the more the person's ambivalence intensifies. Our concern for the person's choices may lead us to persuade, warn, or confront. This stance can rupture the working alliance (*discord*) and the person may decide to stop working with us.

People can talk themselves into or out of change. Rather than pushing against ambivalence, we work to stay out of the "convince/persuade" side of the conversation. Instead, we work to elicit from the person why they want to make the change (*importance*), how they might go about doing so in order to be successful (*confidence*), and under what conditions they might commit to making the change (*readiness*). When both importance and confidence are strong, people are more likely to move toward readiness.

By first accepting and exploring a person's reluctance, we can help them know we are seeking to understand and not just trying to push for change. For example: "I can understand this looks awful to you, that your parents are really pushing you for something you don't want. Tell me what's worst about this; what makes _____ so awful?" Then, once the person feels heard and understood: "What are some exceptions you've thought of to that? How might it be helpful for you to think about trying something different?"

IMAGINING AMBIVALENCE

· · · · · ·

"Ten Meter Tower" is a documentary showcasing a series of individuals contemplating whether or not to jump from a 10-meter diving tower. You might enjoy watching this video and imagining the various competing thoughts and feelings that are happening inside each person as they contemplate jumping from the platform:

https://www.nytimes.com/video/opinion/100000004882589/ten-meter-tower.html.

Supposed to be fun and rewarding, right? Even changes or experiences that take us to a place we imagine to be "better" in some way are not always easy or uncomplicated.

What insights about ambivalence and working with others do you have from watching this video?

_____

_____

_____

_____

_____

What did you notice when someone tried to persuade a person to jump?

_____

_____

_____

_____

_____

What if someone made a motion to push a person off the platform? How do you think the person contemplating the jump might respond?

_____

_____

_____

_____

_____

UNDERSTANDING AMBIVALENCE

· · · · ·

Think about a person with whom you are working. Consider the following questions.

What is on each side of ambivalence for that person? What seems to be pulling them toward making a change (e.g., medication adherence, substance use, physical activity, eating habits)? What is holding them where they are?

_____

_____

_____

_____

_____

How do they share those ideas with you?

_____

_____

_____

_____

_____

How have you shown this person that you see and hear these internal discussions that they are having?

_____

_____

_____

_____

_____

Once that person feels understood, what would you want to elicit from them in order to explore their intrinsic pull toward change?

_____

_____

_____

_____

_____

What if you advocated for change by trying to fix the situation or convince them to use your solution? How could that complicate their internal dialogue and impact their willingness to engage in your work together?

_____

_____

_____

_____

_____

COMPONENTS OF AN EFFECTIVE MOTIVATIONAL CONVERSATION 1: MI-CONSISTENT BEHAVIORS, MI-INCONSISTENT BEHAVIORS, EVOCATIVE BEHAVIORS

Many studies of MI highlight three main components of effective motivational conversations (Miller & Rollnick, 2013). The first component is made up of practitioner behaviors that develop and maintain rapport, most importantly, accurate empathy, compassion, respect, affirmation of strengths, and autonomy support. These *MI-consistent* practitioner behaviors have the quality of *partnering* equally with the person. They support the person's sense of safety and are marked by the person's willingness to explore more deeply the issues under consideration. During this process, the person willingly offers their own values and goals and explores how they are related to the change they are considering.

> For a humorous take on how not to have an MI-consistent conversation, watch this Bob Newhart clip on YouTube: https://www.youtube.com/watch?v=4BjKS1-vjPs

The second component is the absence of *MI-inconsistent* practitioner behaviors. These include confronting the person's perspective, being overly directive by persuading the person without permission, an overreliance on fact-finding questions, or a conversation characterized by a question and answer pattern. These practitioner behaviors decrease the person's sense of safety in the conversation, interrupt self-exploration, and increase ambivalence about exploring the possibility of change.

The third component, *evocative* practitioner behaviors, focuses on identifying and exploring the person's goals, values, and ideas about specific change behaviors. These practitioner behaviors guide the person's exploration to identify a specific *focus* and direction for change, increase the person's exploration of the benefits of change, and evoke their good ideas for making the change.

REFLECTING ON SUPPORTING SELF-EXPLORATION

· · · · · ·

Recall a recent conversation you've had with someone you are serving. Where in the conversation did you hear the person self-explore their own perception of their situation, their goals and values, and how these relate to a specific change they are thinking about making? If you're drawing a blank on a good example of this from your practice, imagine a person you've worked with recently that would really benefit from a process of self-exploration. Answer the questions below with the skills and responses you imagine would be part of the process of that conversation.

_____

_____

_____

_____

_____

What specific skills did you use to support their self-exploration of their current situation, experience and perception, goals and values?

_____

_____

_____

_____

_____

What did the person say about making the change? What reasons or need did they have for making the change? What good ideas did they have for making the change?

_____

_____

_____

_____

_____

What specific skills did you use to support their exploration of making the change?

_____

_____

_____

_____

What, if anything, would you do differently in that conversation if you could do it over?

_____

_____

_____

_____

COMPONENTS OF AN EFFECTIVE MOTIVATIONAL CONVERSATION 2: RELATIONAL AND TECHNICAL COMPONENTS

The components of effective motivational interventions are interrelated and can be categorized as "relational" and "technical." These components are sometimes referred to as the *heartset* and *mindset* of MI.

Relational Components

From the relational perspective, MI practitioners place the person and the person's own goals and best interests at the center of the conversation about change. Conversations about change are done *for* and *with* the person, not *to* the person. People are the undisputed experts on themselves. Activation of the person's expertise is a key condition for MI. The skillful MI practitioner uses highly developed empathy skills, genuineness, and unconditional positive regard to learn about the person's perspective, priorities, values, life circumstances, ideas about what changes to make, and how to go about it. Two major relational components are *empathy* and *partnership*.

Empathy

Research has shown that high-empathy practitioners have higher rates of successful outcomes. Low-empathy practitioners and practitioners with confrontational styles have higher drop-out rates, higher relapse rates, and poorer change outcomes (Bohart, Elliott, Greenberg, & Watson, 2002; Miller, Benefield, & Tonigan, 1993; Miller & Rollnick, 2013; Moyers & Miller, 2013; Rogers, 1965).

Accurate empathy (Rogers, 1959; Truax & Carkhuff, 1967) involves a commitment to understanding the person's perspective and attunement to the person's unfolding experience during a conversation. Accurate empathy is most often demonstrated through skillful *reflective listening*. The practitioner works to understand the person's perspective by reflecting the person's expressed and unexpressed feelings and thoughts. Working together to understand the person's feelings, thoughts, and concerns consolidates the person's understanding and supports their interest in making the change.

Empathic skillfulness improves outcomes and prevents harm (Moyers & Miller, 2013). The American Psychological Association Task Force on Evidence-Based Therapy Relationships (Norcross & Wampold, 2011) designates empathy as an evidence-based element of the therapeutic relationship and recommends that training programs implement competence-based criteria for educating practitioners in relationship elements. In MI, change conversations are structured to incorporate empathy, genuineness, perspective taking, and calling forth the person's expertise and autonomy.

Partnership

Partnership is a key element in guiding conversations about change as equal experts. Practitioner behaviors during change conversations often seem to emphasize information gathering, providing feedback, giving advice, and directive goal setting. Given the ambivalence naturally present in many conversations about change, these practitioner behaviors increase the likelihood of the person arguing *against* making the change. Furthermore, these behaviors increase the risk of rupturing rapport and decrease the likelihood that the ambivalence will be resolved in the direction of change.

On the other hand, working within a *partnership* can increase the person's self-esteem, self-efficacy, and choice and control in the decision-making process. The practitioner supports the person's self-esteem by:

- Expressing respect for the person and their inherent self-worth.
- Focusing on the role that the behavior plays in the person's life and its impact, rather than viewing the person through a deficit lens (e.g., alcoholic, mental patient, truant, felon).

The practitioner increases the person's sense of self-confidence or self-efficacy (Bandura, 1994) by:

- Expressing belief in the person's inherent wisdom and ability to choose a healthier path.
- Affirming the person's strengths, skills, efforts, and intentions.

The practitioner increases the person's *choice and control* by (Brehm & Brehm, 1981; Deci, 1980):

- Supporting the person's responsibility and capability to make their own decisions about the proper course of action.
- Respectfully offering expert information and advice about what has helped others and supporting the person's exploration of how that information or advice fits with their own situation.
- Creating opportunities for the person to consider their choices in light of their values and what they hold as most important in their lives.

Technical Components

On the technical side, practitioners guide the conversation so that the person's ideas about the change and how to go about it take center stage. Effective MI practitioners help people discover their own path toward change and resolve their ambivalence by paying careful attention to how the person *talks* about the change they are considering (i.e., cultivating *change talk* and softening *sustain talk*).

Cultivating Change Talk

Cultivating change talk begins when the person identifies a specific change focus and direction for change. MI practitioners support the person in resolving their ambivalence about change by responding *selectively* to what the person says about making the change (*change talk*). Examples of change talk include:

- "I want to make a change."
- "I'm able to make a change."
- "I have good reasons to make a change."
- "I need to make a change."
- "I will make a change."
- "I am ready to make a change."
- "I've already started taking steps to make the change."

The practitioner looks for opportunities to reinforce the person's exploration of their own change talk and guides the conversation toward the person's exploration of their own commitment to making the change. MI practitioners skillfully evoke change talk, recognize change talk when it occurs, and know how to respond in ways that will build the person's change talk.

Softening Sustain Talk

When guiding toward resolving ambivalence about a change a person is contemplating, MI practitioners avoid strengthening talk about keeping things the same (*sustain talk*). Examples of sustain talk include:

- "I don't want to make a change."
- "I'm not able to make a change."
- "I don't have good reasons to make a change."
- "I don't need to make a change."
- "I will not make a change."
- "I am not ready to make a change."
- "I've already started taking steps to not make the change."

MI practitioners recognize sustain talk when it occurs, seek to understand how the sustain talk is related to the person's concerns about the change under consideration, and respond to sustain talk in ways that soften it. The aim here is to reduce the person's sense of feeling stuck by being pulled in two directions and instead support the person's focus on how they might move forward.

BRIEF CONVERSATIONS ABOUT CHANGE

A question we frequently hear is, What if I only have 5 minutes? We all want the best for those we serve, and we often feel a time crunch. Some of us work in settings that allow for only the briefest of exchanges. These situations often induce stress. We can try to flip that stress switch a bit. The mindset here is, "We've got so many important things to do in so little time, we're going to *slow down and listen thoughtfully*. We're going to be really present and do one thing really well." The person we're working with will be able to form stronger insights and explore more meaningfully with our support, rather than with frustration or pressure. We'll lower our own stress levels and get more done.

CREATING SPACE IN BRIEF CONVERSATIONS

• • • • • •

This exercise starts with a reflection on your own experience of time in several situations and explores the counterintuitive experience of going *slow* or listening thoughtfully in order to accomplish an important task when time is short.

Describe a time when you noticed that taking a deep breath and pausing before launching into something gave you a spaciousness that was not there before.

_____

_____

_____

_____

_____

Describe a time when you noticed that feeling (or acting) like you have all the time in the world let you approach something in a more relaxed way and get more done in a shorter time.

_____

_____

_____

_____

_____

Describe a time when you noticed that hurrying added to your stress and made it more difficult to find your own flow in a situation.

_____

_____

_____

_____

_____

Describe a time when you noticed that trying to hurry someone else made the task take much longer. Or that hurrying generated stumbles that otherwise wouldn't have occurred.

_____

_____

_____

_____

_____

Describe a time when you noticed that not hurrying made things go more smoothly, time seemed to stretch a bit, and you were able to approach the situation with more compassion, acceptance, and effectiveness.

_____

_____

_____

_____

_____

Even though some conversations must be short, we can partner, listen thoughtfully, and bring out motivation for change. Our ability to convey acceptance and compassion, even in brief conversations, strengthens the helping relationship. Consider this brief conversation between a case manager and the person she's just welcomed into the office.

Case Manager: "Hey Sue, how've you been?"

Sue: "Good. My daughter brought the grandbabies to visit. They're a handful, but it's fun."

Case Manager: "It sounds like fun; you must be excited about that!"

Sue: "Yeah, I am."

Case Manager: "How are you doing since your appointment with the psychiatrist?"

Sue: "I'm not doing so well. Julie [her daughter] is pretty mad at me right now."

Case Manager: "She's a bit worried about you."

Sue: "Yeah. I promised her I would take the meds. But I had to tell her the truth: I haven't filled the prescription. She's not very happy about it."

Case Manager: "How do you feel about it?"

Sue: "Honestly? Sometimes I think it's not that big a deal, like I just feel okay. But we've talked about how it starts with thinking I can keep it under control and that's when I lose control, buy too much stuff, don't sleep, and then just crash. But I'm not looking forward to the side effects."

Case Manager: "It's not easy for you to take the meds and at the same time you'd really like to stay on a more even keel."

Sue: "Exactly! I mean, I pretty much know I need to. I can easily pick up the prescription. I probably should before Julie refuses to let me see the kids again."

Case Manager: "You're feeling like it's time to go ahead and try out those meds."

Sue: "Yeah, I mean... it's funny, all these years of ups and downs. But Julie and the kids are more important. She doesn't need to worry about me on top of taking care of them."

Case Manager: "You're really feeling like it's something you can do for yourself, and it will be one less thing for Julie to worry about. You're feeling like it's the right time to take the meds."

Sue: "Yeah, I have to. It's the right thing to do."

Case Manager: "Tell me about that, what does doing 'the right thing' look like for you?"

Sue: "Well, I know the pharmacy has my prescription, I'm just going to pick it up after I leave here. I'm hoping it will help me stay on my budget—you know, pay my rent and my bills and buy food. Keep avoiding those other stores, all the little things I like to buy..."

This quick conversation, less than 5 minutes, began with an almost casual check-in. Even though the time is limited, the case manager is able to open space for the person to explore a change from an earlier conversation. By expressing interest in the person's values, goals, and some next steps, the case manager helps the person increase her own motivation to follow through on her treatment goals.

Here are a variety of conversation starters for a brief MI-consistent conversation. The idea here is to follow these prompts with high-quality, person-centered listening skills like reflective listening and affirmations.

- "I realize our time is short today. I want to make sure I understand what is important to you; what brings you in? Please tell me."
- "Since we have just a few minutes, I'd like to hear about your dilemmas and concerns today."
- "I know you have a lot on your mind today, and we have about five minutes to talk. Let's talk about what's of greatest importance to you, if that's okay with you."
- "We only have about five minutes today. Let's start with what's on your mind, and before we close there's something I wanted to ask you about."
- "Since we need to review your labs today in our short time, let's start with what's important to you, and then I have one thing I'd like to run by you."
- "We have a short time today. I'm particularly curious to hear how important it is for you to consider x going forward."
- "You had been thinking about a change that's pretty important to you. If you're interested we could briefly explore your confidence, the skills, and the capacities you would bring to this change if you decided to do it."
- "I know we have just five minutes today, so maybe it makes sense to focus on your highest priority."

BRIEF CONVERSATION STARTERS

• • • • • •

What other brief conversation starters can you think of?

_____

_____

_____

_____

_____

_____

_____

_____

_____

_____

_____

_____

_____

_____

_____

INTRODUCING MI PROCESSES AND CORE SKILLS

Conversations about change occur within the framework of MI *processes* and use MI *core skills*. The four processes (engaging, focusing, evoking, and planning) help us guide conversations about change. MI core skills (open questions, affirmations, reflections, and summaries) help us stay within the spirit of MI (i.e., partnering, acceptance, compassion, and evocation) while we guide conversations about change.

Within the four processes, the relationship is built first (*engaging*), and change focuses are identified and prioritized (*focusing*) before *evoking* and *planning* can take place. The more complex or interrelated the change focuses are, the longer it can take to navigate the processes for each change focus. Ambivalence often intensifies as the person moves closer to making a change, and discord can easily arise.

Change is not linear, and the four processes are often applied more than once. The natural ambivalence people experience when they consider making a change requires us to understand when we need to *guide forward* to the next process and when we need to *guide back* into an earlier process. This is the dance of MI: flexibility in guiding conversations about change based on the person's *signals* about how the conversation is going.

Some conversations about change are more complex than others. This complexity can be due to multiple change focuses that are interrelated and long-standing. People who are experiencing interrelated mental health, health, and addiction issues may experience significant ambivalence about making a change. Often a change in one focus area will require changes in other areas as well. Initial avoidance can set in motion a cycle of intensifying helplessness and hopelessness that undermine the person's belief in their own ability to change and in the importance of change. Conversations can easily become difficult as the person experiences frustration, anger, or fear about talking about change. The processes help us navigate each change conversation through the rough patches and *build the relationship* (e.g., deepening trust, reliability, empathy, genuineness, and authenticity). As trust and understanding increase, the person can more easily resolve their own ambivalence and build their motivation for change.

Two Guiding Metaphors

When practitioners guide conversations using the four processes, the conversation can vary in complex ways as a function of the person's perspective and experience of their change goals. These different levels of complexity can be described through two metaphors: hiking and dancing.

Hiking

Some conversations about change are simple to guide: Like a well-marked hiking trail, it is easy to stay on the path, and the obstacles are easy to navigate. The person already knows what they want to change, their change focus is consistent with the practitioner's agenda, and they have an easy time deciding how they want to go about it. In these circumstances, the journey from engaging to planning can move along fairly quickly. The practitioner supports the person's exploration of change, builds their momentum, and recognizes when and how the person is ready to create a plan they are committed to following.

However, some conversations, like some hikes, can go off the trail, have unmarked paths, unclear destinations, and unanticipated obstacles. The four processes function much like a compass in these situations, helping us to track our progress in guiding the conversation and to collaborate with the person to decide what needs to be explored next to move closer to the person's goal. The four processes support us in finding a smoother path when the going gets rough or doubling back when needed, without losing sight of the destination.

Dancing

Sometimes, conversations do not follow the four processes in a linear fashion, and the practitioner has to step back to an earlier process to honor changes in a person's ambivalence. When this occurs, we are experiencing the dance of MI: the flexibility in shifting back and forth between the processes based on the person's *signals* about how the conversation is going and what, how, and when they want to make a change. The next five chapters take a deep dive into the core skills and processes.

CHAPTER SUMMARY

• • • • • •

What do you see as this chapter's most important points?

_____

_____

_____

_____

_____

What interested you the most?

_____

_____

_____

_____

_____

What information seemed most relevant to your practice?

_____

_____

_____

_____

_____

THE CORE SKILLS OF MI

The most basic and powerful way to connect to another person is to listen. Just listen.

—Rachel Naomi Remen

IN THIS CHAPTER

- Listening
- Core Skill: Open Questions
- Core Skill: Affirmations
- Core Skill: Reflections
- Core Skill: Summaries
- Offering MI-Consistent Information and Advice
- The Core Skills and the Spirit of MI

The core skills of MI are open questions, affirmations, reflections, and summaries (OARS). We also include how to provide information and advice in an MI-consistent way as part of this chapter because it plays an important role in many conversations about change.

LISTENING

Before we get into the four core skills, it's important to understand that *empathic listening* is the foundation for all the skills. When we really listen, we make space for the other person's authenticity to come forward. Listening with an open and curious heart (a *receptive presence*) allows the other person to experience acceptance, and that can reduce their suffering. A receptive presence emerges from a desire to listen to *understand*, not *respond*. These four steps can help us to listen well in conversations where we want to support the person's exploration of their experiences and aspirations:

1. Form the intention to listen with an open, curious, and nonjudgmental heart. Listen not just with your ears, but with your heart.

2. Notice what is happening inside yourself:

   – Be aware of your own reactions to the conversation and accept what is happening in your inner state as reality.

   – Relax into acceptance of your inner reality and pay close attention to the other person.

3. Ask yourself about the person you are listening to: Who are they? Why are they responding in a particular way? What can you sense about them?

4. Open your receptive presence to the person. Your receptive presence creates a safe space for the person to speak about what has happened to them and who they want to become.

WHAT MAKES A GOOD LISTENER?

• • • • • •

Bring to mind someone you think is a good listener and describe them.

_____

_____

_____

_____

_____

_____

_____

_____

_____

_____

_____

_____

_____

Some adjectives that might have come to mind include "present," "respectful," "self-aware," "nonjudgmental," "caring," "compassionate," "open," and "receptive."

YOUR LISTENING STRENGTHS

· · · · · ·

What do you already do to prepare to listen well *before* a conversation about change?

_____

_____

_____

_____

_____

During a conversation about change?

_____

_____

_____

_____

_____

Name a quality that you aspire to from the previous exercise and describe how you could embody that quality more in your current practice:

_____

_____

_____

_____

_____

Roadblocks to Listening

We often don't listen deeply and openly; for example, when we are distracted, anxious, or feel a need to protect or defend. Sometimes we find it difficult to set aside our own perspective, to really *be there* alongside another person. Sometimes we jump directly to the urge to fix, solve, or advise. To commit ourselves to listening deeply, it helps to know what is getting in the way. This can give us the *option* to truly listen.

Roadblocks to listening were first identified by Thomas Gordon (1970) and later described more fully by Miller and Rollnick (1991). The term "roadblock" describes how certain practitioner behaviors interrupt listening to the flow of the person's self-exploration. When we are using a roadblock, we are neither available to listen nor able to guide. Roadblocks create a barrier the person must navigate before they can get back to their own exploration of the change under consideration. Roadblocks typically communicate an expert stance, a judgment, or a lack of focus. The idea here is even though we intend to be helpful when using roadblocks, it makes the person feel like they are not being listened to. Roadblocks make the person have to work harder for their change. Figure 3 offers examples of roadblocks.

Roadblock	Examples
Ordering or directing	"Stop procrastinating and do something."
Warning or threatening	"If you don't stop… you'll be sorry."
Advising without permission	"I think you need to…"
Persuading	"This is something that could really help you."
"Should-ing" and "ought-ing" (moralizing or preaching)	"You should make sure…"
Judging, blaming, arguing	"You never do what you say…"
Praising, agreeing, approving	"You're really smart; that's exactly what I would do."
Name calling, labeling	"You did that? That's really stupid."
Interpreting, analyzing	"You're just rebelling against…"
Reassuring, consoling	"I'm sure it will work out."
Questioning, probing, interrogating	"Why did you do that instead of what we talked about?"
Withdrawing, humoring, changing the subject	"That's not important. We can talk about that later."

Figure 3. Roadblocks to Listening

WHAT GETS IN THE WAY OF LISTENING?

• • • • • •

Think about a recent conversation, either at work or in your personal life, in which you felt you were *not* listening deeply. Run through the conversation and note where you weren't listening. Ask yourself what interfered and pulled you away from the conversation.

- Was there not enough time?

- Did you want to be somewhere else? To do something else?

- Were you feeling anxious or intimidated?

- Did you want something from them, like approval or cooperation?

- Was there a feeling of being superior or inferior?

- Was there a desire to control the conversation or make something happen?

- Were you distracted by your own thoughts?

- Was there a fear of not existing for the other person (not being seen)?

- Was there a fear that you would not have something to say back?

Even relatively brief periods of listening can bring healing and allow people to consider making changes in their lives.

CORE SKILL: OPEN QUESTIONS

Open questions are those that evoke more than just factual information or "yes/no" responses. For example, "In what ways was *x* helpful to you?" instead of "Was *x* helpful to you?" High-quality open questions guide away from shame and blame—or suggesting there is a "right" answer—and instead evoke thoughtful, strengths-filled responses that naturally support the person's exploration of what, how, and when they might choose to change. Open questions communicate interest in the person's perspective, enhancing the process of engaging.

Collaborative, open questions offer many benefits over fact-finding or history-gathering questions (Robinson & Heritage, 2006):

- Practitioners who ask open collaborative questions are rated as better listeners.
- Collaborative open questions give priority to the person's information and support the person's engagement in the conversation.
- People offer more complete and accurate information in response to open and collaborative questions and are less likely to share important information in response to fact-finding questions.
- People elaborate on their concerns (e.g., needs, symptoms, fears, social and lifestyle concerns) in ways that support tailoring advice and interventions, and lead to positive outcomes.
- People are more likely to engage in the conversation about change and follow through on good ideas for initiating and maintaining change when they are active participants in the change conversation.

What do open questions sound like?

- "What can I do for you today?"
- "How can I be helpful?"
- "How have you been feeling lately?"
- "Tell me how you will use the information or resources you asked about."
- "How would this benefit you?"
- "How will you remember to take your medication as prescribed?"
- "What do you find works well for you to fit these behaviors into your day?"

What do open questions *not* sound like?

- "Is this working for you?"
- "Are you having trouble taking your medications on time?"
- "Do you know you need to…?"
- "Have you been doing…?"

- "Are you feeling okay today?"
- "Does that sound okay?"
- "Okay?"

Following open questions, the practitioner's task is to affirm, reflect, and/or summarize to continue guiding the person's exploration.

CONSIDERING OPEN QUESTIONS

• • • • • •

Think about a person you have seen only once or twice. Considering what you already know about their struggles, strengths, and possible goals, what do you still want to know more about?

_____

_____

_____

_____

_____

How could you phrase open questions to gain more information about what is going on with them?

_____

_____

_____

_____

_____

Modifying Open Questions

Sometimes open questions may be *too* open or overwhelming to answer for people who, for example, experience thought disorders or cognitive limitations. We can modify open questions to make them easier for people to respond by:

- Breaking down complex open questions into separate, simpler open questions. For example, "Tell me about your experience of sadness and how your medications help or don't help" becomes two questions: "Tell me about your experience of sadness," and "What effect do your medications have on your experience?"

- Simplifying complex open questions by *normalizing* the question, offering a variety of options, and then asking a narrower question. For example, rather than "Tell me about ways you manage your anxious feelings," we might say, "Everyone manages their feelings of anxiety differently—some do *x*, *y*, or *z*. How would you say it is for you?"

"Why" questions can also be problematic. They require more abstract information processes and can create confusion and defensiveness. These questions can be broken down to the most important information. For example, "Why were you hospitalized?" becomes "What are the main reasons you were hospitalized?"

"Why" questions can also lead to a need to defend or explain the past or the status quo and can be judgmental. If we ask "why" about a past action or a current situation, such as "Why did you do it that way?" or "Why was it hard for you to get here on time today?" the person would be in a position of defending the situation. However, "why" asked about the future can be effective. "Why might you, if you decided to do this?" or "Why would it be helpful for you to have reliable transportation?" invites the person to speculate about a change topic in a more envisioning way.

Finally, if the person struggles to respond to open questions, *modified closed questions* with menus of response options help to normalize choices and support the person's autonomy and their ability to respond. For example: "You mentioned that you might like to work. Some people prefer to work outside, some like to work with the public, and others want to work at a desk. What do you prefer?"

CORE SKILL: AFFIRMATIONS

An *affirmation* is a comment on or reflection of something you genuinely admire or value about a person that is both accurate and observable, such as their intentions, actions, skills, character, worth, insights, effort, and values. Affirmations usually center on the word "you" and guide conversations about change by bringing forward the person's true *capabilities* and *strengths*. These characteristics support the person's exploration of their own wisdom, experience, and good ideas as they consider the change focus. It can be helpful to also consider a person's vulnerabilities and challenges when looking for ways to affirm them.

Genuine and *specific* affirmations of the person's efforts, intentions, strengths, and skills can shift how a person sees themselves, cultivating hope and strengthening recovery capacity. Affirmations can help to reduce anxiety and discord and increase rapport. As people talk about their experiences, what they are doing to manage their distress, what is important to them, and what their goals are, they offer many opportunities for affirmations:

- "I see your commitment to feeling less anxious and distracted. You've already come up with some good ideas that you are trying out. This is really important to you."

- "Thank you for your honesty about your concerns about our work together and your past treatment experiences. You are committed to getting what you need. Where would you like to start first?"

- "You are willing to do what it takes to have your family involved in your plan. It's your choice how we talk with them about it. What do you feel will work best for you?"

- "I understand that you did not want to be here, and I appreciate that you've agreed to talk with me. I'm looking forward to working together with you to see how we can make this a helpful way for you to reach your goals."

Affirmations shine a spotlight on the positive. We take on an affirming stance when we are on a consistent treasure hunt for positive qualities, efforts, and capacities. Affirmations come from a position of respect, regard, and generosity for others. High-quality affirmations that reframe a person's perceived weakness as a genuine strength can powerfully shift a person's self-concept to be even more capable and strong. We particularly want to avoid emphasizing feelings of hopelessness and negative experiences at the end of a conversation, preferring to end with strengths, appreciation, and looking forward to what the person plans to do next. As William James wrote, "The deepest principle in human nature is the craving to be appreciated." Affirmations:

- Demonstrate appreciation to others.

- Reduce defensiveness, increase engagement, reinforce positive qualities, and increase the likelihood that the person will use those qualities more often.

- Set a positive tone for our interactions, increase a willingness for information exchange and activation, and facilitate possibilities for change.

- Increase hope and confidence and reduce defensiveness.

The Strengths of Successful Changers tool can help you and the person with whom you are working collaboratively identify their positive qualities and strengths. You may want to make copies of this tool; we will use it again in later chapters.

STRENGTHS OF SUCCESSFUL CHANGERS

• • • • •

Accepting	Committed	Flexible	Persevering	Stubborn
Active	Competent	Focused	Persistent	Thankful
Adaptable	Concerned	Forgiving	Positive	Thorough
Adventuresome	Confident	Forward-looking	Powerful	Thoughtful
Affectionate	Considerate	Free	Prayerful	Tough
Affirmative	Courageous	Happy	Quick	Trusting
Alert	Creative	Healthy	Reasonable	Trustworthy
Alive	Decisive	Hopeful	Receptive	Truthful
Ambitious	Dedicated	Imaginative	Relaxed	Understanding
Anchored	Determined	Ingenious	Reliable	Unique
Assertive	Die-hard	Intelligent	Resourceful	Unstoppable
Assured	Diligent	Knowledgeable	Responsible	Vigorous
Attentive	Doer	Loving	Sensible	Visionary
Bold	Eager	Mature	Skillful	Whole
Brave	Earnest	Open	Solid	Willing
Bright	Effective	Optimistic	Spiritual	Winning
Capable	Energetic	Orderly	Stable	Wise
Careful	Experienced	Organized	Steady	Worthy
Cheerful	Faithful	Patient	Straight	Zealous
Clever	Fearless	Perceptive	Strong	Zestful

Source: Miller, 2004.

"Scaffolding" Affirmations

An effective way to build MI skillfulness is by gradually building a skill level by level, or *scaffolding*. For example, we can strengthen our ability to affirm the people we serve starting with affirming people who are easy to affirm and shifting into affirming people who are more challenging to affirm. We can "warm up" our affirmation skills by first practicing *self*-affirmation before practicing affirming others.

SELF-AFFIRMATION

· · · · · ·

Identify *at least* 10 strengths or qualities that are true for you. You can use the Strengths of Successful Changers tool to help you create your list.

_____

_____

_____

_____

_____

Think about the ways you used those qualities to accomplish something difficult in your life. Write a description of what you accomplished and the strengths and qualities you used to be successful.

_____

_____

_____

Describe how you use those qualities on a daily basis.

_____

_____

_____

How could you use those qualities to get started on (or to accomplish) a change that you've been considering?

_____

_____

_____

STRENGTHENING OUR AFFIRMING SKILLS

• • • • • •

Level 1: Easy Affirmations

Bring to mind someone you know who is easy to love and appreciate. What are some of this person's natural vulnerabilities, fears, losses, and sorrows?

_____

_____

_____

_____

_____

What are some of this person's strengths, skills, and intentions?

_____

_____

_____

_____

_____

Imagine saying something to them about what you see and appreciate in them. Center your affirmations around the word "you" (e.g., "You've really given this a lot of thought"). You can use the Strengths of Successful Changers tool to help you create your affirmations.

Affirmations:

_____

_____

_____

_____

_____

Level 2: More Challenging Affirmations

Bring to mind someone else that you care about but with whom you experience some static in the relationship. Stretch yourself to sense their natural vulnerability, fears, losses, and self-doubt.

What vulnerabilities do you sense that this person has, which are similar to those that you experience in the relationship?

_____

_____

_____

_____

_____

What are their strengths, skills, and intentions?

_____

_____

_____

_____

_____

Imagine saying something to them about what you see and appreciate in them (e.g., "Even though it's been difficult, you've really persisted with finding a solution here").

Affirmations:

_____

_____

_____

_____

_____

Level 3: Very Challenging Affirmations

Bring to mind someone who is hard for you to care about and with whom you feel tense and/or distant. Remember that so many of us live with loss, feelings of failure, self-doubt, our own vulnerability, and not knowing what is going to happen next.

With deep compassion for yourself, list some of your own thoughts and feelings (e.g., hurt, anger, blame) that may be conjured up by this relationship.

_____

_____

_____

_____

Access the small, vulnerable place within, and attend to what it needs (e.g., understanding, forgiveness, care). As you feel yourself shift into a larger space filled with awareness and compassion, envision the person's vulnerability and dilemma. Notice how similar their experience of vulnerability is to your own. Stretch yourself to see their strengths, skills, and intentions.

Imagine saying something to them about what you see and appreciate in them (e.g., "Even though it is not what you want to be doing, you are really doing your best here, and that hasn't been easy").

Affirmations:

_____

_____

_____

_____

You may want to commit to consciously practicing each level of affirmation in the change conversations you will have in the coming week.

CORE SKILL: REFLECTIONS

Reflections are fundamental to MI because they help guide conversations about change by developing an increasingly *accurate understanding* of a person's wants and needs. Reflections are used to respectfully highlight a thought or feeling, respond to reluctance about change or discomfort within the working relationship, and gently guide challenging conversations. It is not always easy to tell how accurately we have captured a person's experience. We will sometimes unintentionally misinterpret something the person has said. People are more likely to gently correct our misunderstandings and continue on with their exploration when we are guiding the conversation with reflections filled with genuine and compassionate interest in what the person *means*. Sometimes we revise our reflections in mid-sentence in response to slight cues. Our effort to understand demonstrates our positive regard for the person and their self-worth. Although in the moment we may feel that listening is not enough, to the person this slender connection may be everything.

The research-based standard for an MI conversation is *a ratio of at least 2:1 reflections to questions, with at least 50 percent of our reflections being complex*. This standard helps us consider how we might want to shift our use of reflections to better guide the person's exploration and resolution of ambivalence about change. If we notice that we're using too many questions based on the ratio, that may help us realize that we are tipping the balance toward ourselves as experts instead of viewing the person as the expert on themselves. We may also notice that when we ask too many questions, the person explores less and offers less accurate and helpful information. Checking how we are balancing the core skills helps us consider how we might shift our skills for even better outcomes. Reflections can be *simple* or *complex*.

Simple Reflections

Simple reflections ensure and communicate that we are following what the person is saying. A simple reflection repeats or slightly rephrases something a person says. Simple reflections can highlight an important or significant feeling or thought that emerges during a conversation *without adding to the content or meaning*. Because a person talks more about what we reflect, we can use simple reflections to gently guide the person to further explore something they've said.

Complex Reflections

Complex reflections capture what we think the person *means* by adding our guess about meaning to what we hear the person say. Complex reflections are genuine and accurate best guesses that guide the person's exploration toward *deeper* understanding, *broader* consideration of options, or *forward* toward resolving ambivalence about change (Wagner & Ingersoll, 2013, p. 41). Complex reflections:

- Communicate acceptance that behaviors, beliefs, emotions, and patterns are understandable, adaptive, and necessary based on the person's experience. This increases self-compassion.

- Broaden the person's view of the behavior and their view of themselves into a larger, more strengths-based context.

- Reframe the person's perception of behaviors, beliefs, emotions, and patterns in their life as something they can change if they choose to.

Depth Reflection

A depth reflection can guide toward deeper exploration. One example of an effective depth reflection is the use of a *metaphor* or *simile* to capture more of the person's whole experience by painting a picture (e.g., "It's like you're caught between a rock and a hard place"). A reflection that paints a picture of the person's ambivalence communicates what we understand about the person's experience and makes it easier for the person to consider. From this vantage point they can clarify and build on the mutual understanding.

Breadth Reflection

Complex reflections guide more broadly to open up the exploration to see what direction the person wants to go (e.g., "…and you're wondering about your options here." "You have some ideas about where you might want to start.").

Forward Reflection

We use forward reflections to communicate understanding and acceptance while guiding toward an important next step in the person's consideration of the change. Forward reflections capture change talk as it emerges and help with resolving ambivalence. When we are so attuned to the person's experience that we genuinely believe we can accurately describe the person's next thought or feeling, we might use a forward reflection (e.g., "…and that's what really worries you about this").

Reframing Reflection

A reframing reflection transforms barriers or concerns into challenges and opportunities while honoring the person's perspective:

> **Person:** "I would try another medication, but they're so expensive,"
>
> **Practitioner:** "You're open to trying something new that fits your budget."

Examples of Complex Reflections: Scenario

Sally thinks she wants to try to quit smoking cigarettes again. She can't quite describe why she still smokes: "I don't know, it's relaxing maybe?" She also describes her smoking as "sneaking" and hides it from her family. When she discusses returning to smoking after months of not smoking, she says, "I don't know why I went back. I wish I hadn't. I wish they would just quit making them, and then I wouldn't have to make myself quit."

Complex reflections (depth, breadth, forward, reframing) can help guide a conversation with Sally that supports her in developing awareness of her triggers for smoking and some options for managing those triggers.

> **Sally:** "I feel like I'm sneaking, you know? I wish they'd stop making them, and then I wouldn't have to make myself quit. You know what I mean? That would be great."
>
> **Practitioner:**
>
> *Forward Reflection:* "You want to stop smoking."
>
> *Depth Reflection:* "You want to model healthier behaviors for your kids."
>
> *Breadth Reflection:* "You're looking for some good options for quitting."

Reframing Reflection: "It's easier to quit when you know they just aren't available. You're looking for a way to quit without feeling like you're depriving yourself."

Sally: "I don't know; I just got sick of it, of smoking. I got tired of it and then…last time I quit I had the flu. I do enjoy it. That's one of the problems, I think. It relaxes you or something. I don't know. I don't know why I started up again, I wish I hadn't."

Practitioner:

Forward Reflection: "When you quit this time, you want to quit for good."

Depth Reflection: "You want to understand more about why you smoke so you can quit for good."

Breadth Reflection: "You already have some experience quitting smoking, and you're looking for even more ideas.

Reframing Reflection: "It's important to you to have other ways to relax and enjoy yourself when you quit this time."

Sally: "I think what will make me quit is the money I spend on cigarettes. I want to get some things for my kids."

Practitioner:

Forward Reflection: "You want to quit to be able to afford more things for your family."

Depth Reflection: "You see a connection between being able to do more for your family and quitting smoking. This is really important to you."

Breadth Reflection: "You're looking for some good options for quitting because you are seeing how much it's costing you in terms of your health, your family, and your finances."

Reframing Reflection: "Quitting would help you do more for them and for yourself."

Sally: "Yeah, you know, sometimes you get some crappy news, and you just go and have a smoke."

Practitioner:

Forward Reflection: "You want to be able to handle crappy news without smoking again."

Depth Reflection: "You know one thing that makes you smoke is when you get bad news. It undermines your sense of peace and well-being and makes you want to smoke."

Breadth Reflection: "You want to find some good options for dealing with crappy news without smoking."

Reframing Reflection: "One of the challenges you want to master is dealing with bad news without smoking."

COMPLEX REFLECTIONS

· · · · · ·

How might you continue guiding this conversation with Sally? Try generating some more examples of what Sally might say next and then create reflections to see where you might guide the conversation.

Sally:

_____

_____

_____

_____

Forward Reflection:

_____

_____

_____

_____

_____

Breadth Reflection:

_____

_____

_____

_____

_____

Depth Reflection:

_____
_____
_____
_____
_____

Reframing Reflection:

_____
_____
_____
_____
_____

Sally:

_____
_____
_____
_____
_____

Forward Reflection:

_____
_____
_____
_____
_____

Breadth Reflection:

_____
_____
_____
_____
_____

Depth Reflection:

_____

_____

_____

_____

Reframing Reflection:

_____

_____

_____

_____

Sally:

_____

_____

_____

_____

Forward Reflection:

_____

_____

_____

_____

Breadth Reflection:

_____

_____

_____

_____

_____

Depth Reflection:

_____

_____

_____

_____

_____

Reframing Reflection:

_____

_____

_____

_____

_____

Sally:

_____

_____

_____

_____

_____

Forward Reflection:

_____

_____

_____

_____

Breadth Reflection:

_____

_____

_____

_____

Depth Reflection:

_____

_____

_____

_____

Reframing Reflection:

_____

_____

_____

_____

When people experience distressing symptoms, we can use reflections to invite them to observe their own beliefs and behaviors and consider learning new ways to cope. Simple reflections help people who experience cognitive impairment remember what's already been discussed and consider what they want to do next. When working with people who experience thought disorders, simple reflections help the person consider their experience, how it has changed over time, and how observing their experiences (e.g., delusions, auditory hallucinations) can help them make progress toward their life goals. For example:

> **Practitioner:** "You mentioned that it really bothers you when you feel like people are laughing at you. At the same time, it sounds like you think there is a possibility that people might *not* have been laughing at you. What makes you think that?"
>
> **Person:** "I don't know, when I saw they were laughing, then I started thinking they were laughing at me."
>
> **Practitioner:** "So you remember having the thought after you saw them laughing. Could you tell me more about that? Why do you think it's possible you made a mistake there?"
>
> **Person:** "Well, I was pretty upset. Things were pretty bad at home. My sister says I read into things people are doing when I'm upset."
>
> **Practitioner:** "What do you think about that?"
>
> **Person:** "I'm not sure, I'll have to think about it."

REFLECTIVE STATEMENT STARTERS

• • • • • •

Effective reflective statements are closely tailored to the person's words and intended meaning. *Reflective statement starters* help us get into the flow of reflective listening and offer ways to vary the sound of our statements. Here are some examples:

- "This has been totally ___ for you in that…"
- "It's more like ___ than ___ for you."
- "It's almost as if…"
- "As you see it, …"
- "I get the sense that…"
- "Like a…"
- "I can see that…"
- "For you, …"
- "For you, it's a matter of…"
- "From your point of view…"
- "From your perspective…"
- "I'm getting that you…"
- "I get the impression that you…"
- "I would imagine you…"
- "This is hard for you because…"
- "There's a way this is easy for you because…"
- "When you look at it that way, it seems…"
- "You're looking at this in different ways, such as ___ and ___."

- "Must be…"

- "Through your eyes…"

- "There's a part of you that…"

- "You're already beginning to notice a difference…"

- "Your concern is that…"

- "Your fear is that…"

- "It seems to you that…"

- "You're not terribly excited about…"

- "You're not much concerned that…"

- "You're a little concerned that…"

- "The thing that bothers you is…"

- "What bothers you most about this is…"

- "The important thing for you here is…"

- "I would bet that you…"

- "You're already thinking of ways to make this work such as ___ and ___."

- "You're wondering if…"

- "You're hoping that…"

- "You're really seeing a connection for yourself between ___ and ___."

Modifying Reflections

When people experience disorganized thinking, poor reality testing, or cognitive limitations, it can be helpful to use brief, frequent reflections and summaries to reduce demands on their concentration and memory. Reflections are often focused on affect until more complex reflections can be used. When people experience beliefs about mind control, longer reflection statement starters (or *stems*) help to reinforce the boundary between the person's thoughts and the practitioner's thoughts. For example:

- "It sounds like you feel..."
- "As I listen to what you are saying, it sounds like you _____. Is that right?"
- "Some of the other people I work with hear voices and they sometimes believe the voices belong to someone else. Have you ever felt that way?"

Even when making progress, people often experience bad days (i.e., their symptoms are worse). We can use reflections to increase hope and confidence for coping with these days and maintain a focus on future goals. Rather than dwelling on fixed beliefs and other symptoms, we can use reflections to explore the *impact* of the belief or symptom on the person's life:

Person: "It started as a narrator, strange made it strange, then it became voices of people who hurt me."

Practitioner: "You're saying it started as just a narrator and then something made it seem strange. That's when you started to hear familiar voices and feel scared. Is that right?"

Modified reflections are also used to tie fragmented or disorganized thoughts into coherent ideas and help people observe their own thoughts, beliefs, and experiences. As people become aware that an unusual belief or symptom may not be reality based, they strengthen their ability to consider options for coping with these experiences.

We use longer pauses following reflections and questions to help people process information and track the conversation more easily. We use brief pauses when a person believes they are experiencing mind control, to decrease their concerns about the practitioner reading their mind.

Learning to Reflect

Some of us use few reflections, some of us use many simple reflections but few complex reflections, and some of us already use simple and complex reflections and are working toward guiding with reflections that create forward momentum, depth, and breadth. This is a rich area of practice to explore wherever we are in our current level of skillfulness. There is always more to learn from the people with whom we work. When practicing reflections, it is helpful to breathe, relax, and trust ourselves to make progress toward our goal, while also observing our progress and increasing our learning.

DEEPENING YOUR REFLECTING SKILLS

· · · · · ·

In learning to guide deeper, broader, and forward with complex reflections, it helps to listen to recordings of our own conversations to understand where we want to make changes.

Note: You could also use this exercise as a partner activity by reviewing each other's recordings.

Record a change conversation. Listen to the recording and:

Create a tally sheet and count the number of questions and the number of any type of reflection.

Total questions: _____   Total reflections: _____

Calculate your ratio of questions to reflections: _____

What are your thoughts about your ratio given the suggested ratio of 2:1 reflections to questions?

_____

_____

_____

_____

_____

Listen to your recording again. This time:

Create a tally sheet and count the number of reflections you offered by type: simple and complex.

Total simple reflections: _____   Total complex reflections: _____

What are your thoughts about your use of simple and complex reflections?

_____

_____

_____

_____

What is your sense about how often you used complex reflections that create forward momentum, depth, breadth, or reframing?

_____

_____

_____

_____

Based on your assessments, what goals regarding the use of reflections might you want to set?

_____

_____

_____

_____

You may want to repeat this exercise over time to track your progress.

CORE SKILL: SUMMARIES

Summaries are essentially reflections that pull together what a person has told us. They shine a light on the person's experience and help them remember what they've said in order to reflect on their experiences and options. Summaries can guide toward further exploration in the same direction or consolidate important elements of the exploration before transitioning to another task or topic. Early summaries in MI conversations show that we have been listening carefully, that we value what the person has said, and that we want the person to correct any misunderstanding or fill in what we have missed.

Once a focus and direction of change is established, summaries are typically used to consolidate progress in exploring the change under consideration by capturing the most important parts of the person's ambivalence about change and all of their motivation for change. During the planning process, summaries are part of guiding to strengthen the person's commitment to making the change by pulling together the person's motivations, intentions, and plans for change. Continuing the "Sally" example, a summary might sound like:

> *"Let me just make sure I understand where we are. You're thinking about quitting smoking for your health and your kids. You know the smoking relaxes you and at the same time you get sick of it and see some ways the extra money would help you afford things for your kids that you can't afford now. You've quit before when you had the flu, and you're looking for some ways to do it again and make it stick. Is that right?"*

Modifying Summaries

As with reflections, summaries may need to be modified when people experience disorganized thinking, poor reality testing, or cognitive limitations. Modified summaries are simplified and more frequent. Helpful summaries guide toward:

- Reducing the person's experience of distress and chaos.
- Strengthening the person's ability to observe their experiences, perceptions, and beliefs.
- Increasing the person's functional capacity and momentum for change.

STRENGTHENING OUR SUMMARIZING SKILLS

· · · · · ·

1. Invite a friend or colleague to have a 5-minute discussion with you about a change they are considering or a decision they need to make.

2. At the end of the conversation, take a few minutes to *write* a concise summary of the conversation. Writing first is a way of *scaffolding* learning to summarize. It allows you time to think through the conversation and thoughtfully summarize.

3. Try this exercise several more times, with the same person or different people, writing summaries of the 5-minute conversations.

4. Once you feel comfortable with summarizing, try the exercise again but this time verbally summarize the conversation as you go along.

5. Consider focusing on summarizing in the next change conversation you have with a person with whom you are working.

OFFERING MI-CONSISTENT INFORMATION AND ADVICE

Offering MI-consistent information and advice consists of giving information in a way that supports the person's autonomy and exploration of what, how, and when they might choose to make a change. We avoid direct persuasion or confrontation about what the person should do by infusing information and advice with collaboration and autonomy support. For example:

- Prior to giving information or advice, we work to understand what the person *already knows* about their options or the topic and any specific ideas they are already interested in.

- We tailor our advice or information to the person's knowledge, situation, and preferences.

- To avoid inadvertent persuasion, we frame information and advice in the form of a range of options that have helped others in similar situations.

- When we do make specific recommendations for the person, we emphasize the person's autonomy to choose for themselves.

- After offering information or advice, we invite the person to explore how the information or advice may or may not work for them.

Elicit-provide-elicit (sometimes known as ask-offer-ask or chunk-check-chunk) combines seeking collaboration and emphasizing autonomy:

Elicit: Ask about the person's own ideas and knowledge about the subject. For example:

- "What have you heard about the ways in which people get support to stop using substances?"

- "What ideas do you have for transportation?"

- "What health services would you like to learn more about?"

Provide: If it sounds like some advice or information would still be helpful, provide or offer this advice or information with permission (seeking collaboration). To preserve the collaboration and increase the likelihood that they will give these options some consideration, it's important to give the person more than one option (and acknowledge the person's freedom to disagree or ignore the information or advice). For example:

- "May I make a suggestion?"

- "Would you be interested in knowing about some resources?"

- "I don't know if this would interest you, but some people find…"

Elicit: Ask for their response to the suggestion or information you have provided (seeking collaboration):

- "What do you think of these options for your situation?"

- "You're the expert here, how might these ideas work for you?"

- "Are you interested in trying any of these suggestions?"

Elicit-provide-elicit could look like this:

Practitioner [elicit]: "What do you know about the connection between what people do and how they feel?"

Person: "Well, last time we talked we figured out that I feel better after I do little things, like take a shower."

Practitioner [elicit]: "Right—that's exactly what I'm asking about. What else do you remember?"

Person: "That when I didn't do anything, I felt worse."

Practitioner [provide]: "Yes, you noticed a pattern where mornings before your shower and walk you felt worse, and then after your shower and walk you felt a bit better. We talked about possibly scheduling some more pleasant activities into your week to see how you feel then. What do you think about working on that together today?"

Person: "Um…okay, but do I have to come up with the activities?"

Practitioner [elicit]: "Well, if you want, we can start with your ideas. And then if it's helpful, I can offer some additional ideas that other people have found helpful [potentially provide]. But really, you are the expert on what will work best for you [emphasize autonomy]. What do you think? Should we try this out [seek collaboration]?"

MI-consistent information exchange helps to increase participation in sorting through information and ideas for interventions and activities. Emphasizing the person's expertise about what will work for them helps them bring forward their ideas and avoid passive agreement with our ideas.

This may be particularly true when we are working with young people. Asking permission to explore topics and exchange information demonstrates respect for the person's choices and capabilities. Following new information with interest in their thoughts about how it might fit for them supports autonomy and collaboration. This MI-consistent way of offering information helps us to partner with young people to develop options and solutions. It provides a safe and collaborative environment where they can explore their own thoughts and make decisions.

Avoiding Discord During Information Exchange

When offering information or feedback, we want to avoid triggering discord. We can change our approach to strengthen empathy and acceptance if discord emerges. For example: "It sounds like this doesn't seem relevant to you. What do you feel is most important for us to talk about?" A few strategies for reducing the likelihood of discord when offering information include:

- Asking about what the person already knows and tailoring the information to what the person knows and is interested in changing (i.e., their strengths, goals, and needs).

- Offering information after the person asks for it.

- Asking permission to offer information.

- Supporting collaboration and autonomy (e.g., "You are the only person who can decide what makes the most sense for you in this situation." "I'm interested in your thoughts about how this information applies to your situation.").

ASSESSING INFORMATION EXCHANGE

· · · · · ·

What are some examples of how *you* evoke what the person already knows, ask permission, and support collaboration and autonomy during the information exchange?

_____

_____

_____

_____

_____

How do *you* strengthen empathy and acceptance when discord emerges?

_____

_____

_____

_____

_____

THE CORE SKILLS AND THE SPIRIT OF MI

The core skills are balanced to help us stay within the spirit of MI (i.e., partnering, acceptance, compassion, and evocation). The heartset and mindset of the MI spirit guides the use and practice of the core skills. For example, consider a person struggling with medication adherence who says, "I know I should pay more attention to the meds, but it's just so difficult day after day." It can be tempting to jump in and say, "It shouldn't be too hard, if you just [provide solution]." Instead of minimizing the person's concerns, we use the core skills to honor the person's effort and willingness to talk about their concerns and invite exploration of potential directions for addressing those concerns. For example:

- "You're finding this tough to do."
- "...and that sounds like your biggest challenge right now."
- "You're trying to find a way to do it, since it's something that's important to you."
- "You're hoping we can come up with some ideas together to make this a little easier."
- "I can see how it would be difficult. If you are interested, we can explore possible solutions together."

As we've noted, developing skills to stay within the MI spirit can be seen as a task in scaffolding. We start where we are and use observations (i.e., either in vivo or recording-based) to identify the next skill development steps that will get us closer to our practice goals. Practice developing the skills that make the most sense for you and proceed until you can guide skillfully with:

- 2:1 reflections to questions.
- 50 percent complex reflections to total reflections.
- Evocative questions instead of fact-finding questions.
- Affirmations, invitations to collaborate, and autonomy support.
- Summaries.

CHAPTER SUMMARY

• • • • • •

What do you see as the most important points of this chapter?

_____

_____

_____

_____

What interested you the most?

_____

_____

_____

_____

What core skill(s) do you think you most need/want to work on?

_____

_____

_____

_____

ENGAGING: THE RELATIONAL FOUNDATION

They may forget what you said—but they will never forget how you made them feel.

—Carl W. Buehner

We were created for social connection. We are at our best when we have healthy relationships with people who genuinely care about us, respect us, and lift us up.

—Robyn L. Gobin

IN THIS CHAPTER

- The Importance of Engaging

- Engaging and the Initial MI Conversation

- Our Strengths in Engaging

- Challenges of Engaging

- MI-Consistent Ways to Gather Assessment Information

- Engaging with Open Questions, Affirmations, and Reflections

- Engaging by Exploring Values and Priorities

- Preparing for Engaging Conversations

- Ongoing Assessment of Our Ability to Engage

- The Dance of MI: Introduction to a Framework

- The Dance of MI: Moving from Engaging to Focusing

Engaging is the process of establishing a mutually trusting and respectful helping relationship. It includes understanding the person's perception of their situation and bringing forward the person's strengths, wisdom, and freedom of choice. When engaging, we help people identify goals and collaborate with them on mutually negotiated tasks toward achieving those goals. Our capacity to help a person feel understood and respected sets the stage for engagement.

THE IMPORTANCE OF ENGAGING

Engaging is a necessary foundation for people to activate positive health behaviors. People who are engaged and activated are more willing, able, and ready to invest in their own health-promoting actions, such as seeking preventative care, exercising regularly, and initiating or maintaining other important lifestyle changes and self-management activities. They are also more likely to view us as allies in their change process. People who are engaged:

- Are more interested in our guidance and express higher levels of willingness, ability, and readiness for change.
- Feel heard and understood, feel that their priorities are valued and respected.
- Have stronger health outcomes and are easier and more enjoyable to work with.

Genuine efforts to understand, collaborate, and help people reach their life goals begin with:

- A welcoming word, tone of voice, or opportunity to sit silently together.
- Empathy, collaboration, and refusing interruptions.
- The absence of coercive behaviors.
- Making time to listen to a story about a difficult experience.

Engaging begins even before we begin our first conversation. Offering a warm welcome in a friendly, safe atmosphere is a basic first step. A warm welcome differs depending on our setting, our agenda, and our personal style. Simply offering a beverage can go a long way.

WARM WELCOME

· · · · · ·

What policies or expectations does your agency/practice have in place to ensure a warm welcome for the people you serve? How does the physical environment contribute?

_____

_____

_____

_____

How do you personally welcome a person new to your services?

_____

_____

_____

_____

Do you see any ways in which your agency/you could be more welcoming?

_____

_____

_____

_____

ENGAGING AND THE INITIAL MI CONVERSATION

The first conversation about change is especially important for engaging people into the change process. MI practitioners use the first conversation to develop a mutual understanding of the person's priorities, experiences, perceptions, goals, and good ideas. These are the person's resources that initiate and support their change journey. Change is deeply connected to the values, skills, and motivations the person brings to the situation.

Engagement is enhanced when we offer a *rationale* for talking about change that is infused with the MI spirit and supports the person's autonomy and readiness to make a change. When working with people who feel very ambivalent about making a change, such as people who experience intense anxiety, Westra (2012) recommends including specific points about ambivalence, autonomy, and readiness:

- Ambivalence about change is normal.
- Change is difficult.
- Reasons for making a change and against making a change often emerge together.
- It is the person's decision whether or not to make the change and how they might make the change.

Consider this initial conversation:

> **Practitioner** [asking permission]: "So I wonder if it would be okay to talk about how we usually approach these initial conversations, and then I'd like to hear your thoughts about that."
>
> **Person:** "Okay."
>
> **Practitioner:** "Well first of all, I want you to know that I'm not here to *make* you make a change. We find that when people worry quite a bit, they often feel like it would be good to make a change but at the same time they feel uncertain about whether it's something they actually want to change. What is it like for you?"
>
> **Person:** "I'm relieved to hear you say that because I do *want* to worry less and at the same time, I have some concerns about that. Like it helps me do what I need to do, and I don't know what would motivate me if I didn't worry."
>
> **Practitioner:** "Yes, you feel like it helps, and you feel concern about life without it. That is very common. That's also related to another concern that people sometimes have—that change is difficult. It can be hard to change things that have worked well enough up until now."
>
> **Person:** "Yeah, is that normal too?"
>
> **Practitioner:** "Yup. That is super normal, and we generally find that as we explore those experiences people feel less concern and more ready to try out some things to make a change. You may feel that way, too, and if you do, it will be your choice what options you try out. What do you think about all this?"
>
> **Person:** "Well, it sounds like it won't be easy—and I didn't think it would—so I appreciate your honesty. And you're saying it's my decision so I think we should get started and see how it goes."

Acknowledging the person's perspective is crucial. Acknowledgment is not the same as agreeing or approving. Our *empathy* and *understanding* are key to reducing defensiveness and promoting the person's exploration to facilitate healing and actual change. Empathy is crucial for everyone with whom we work but plays a profoundly important role for some. For example:

- For youth, empathy provides a contrast to the disengagement young people often experience with authority figures and adults in general.
- For a person who has been mandated to treatment, empathy can help heal discord and feelings of unfairness, being judged, and social injustice.
- For a person with a thought disorder, empathy and understanding can ease feelings of being stigmatized, "different" from everyone else, and consequent loneliness.

Consider Leona:

Leona has been referred by her physician because she has been requesting increasingly stronger prescriptions of alprazolam to manage her panic attacks. Leona first reported experiencing intense anxiety and panic following her mother's death six months ago and consistently reports that her panic attacks have intensified. Her prescribing physician believes her anxiety may have worsened at least in part due to increased tolerance to the medication.

Practitioner: "I understand that your doctor recommended that you come in to talk with me. Would it be alright if we talk about what has been happening and your understanding about what's going on?"

Leona: "Thank you for asking for my side of this. I'm really upset about how she is treating me. Just because I need more alprazolam, she thinks I have some kind of 'problem.' That just doesn't make sense to me. I told her I would taper down when things are less stressful. But I need the medication. She just doesn't understand how bad my anxiety is right now."

Practitioner: "It sounds like your doctor wants to taper you off of the alprazolam—and you have some concerns about that, you don't agree with her."

Leona: "Yeah, it's like all of a sudden I'm some kind of addict! I'm no addict, I am a department head at work, I have an assistant, I take good care of my children, and my life isn't easy. I take my medication as prescribed. I don't even drink, but now I'm starting to wish I did!"

Practitioner: "This feels unfair. You feel you've been doing everything you are supposed to do and it seems like she isn't seeing that—and she isn't hearing how much distress you are in."

Leona: "Right! And her timing is unbelievable! Right when I'm having even more trouble sleeping, and my hands are shaking…I need a higher dose to manage this. I can't believe she's pushing this taper on me. It's harder and harder to get through my day."

Practitioner: "It sounds like it's been an especially difficult time since even before you spoke with your doctor."

Leona [tearing up]: "I've been struggling to get the kids to school on time. They are having a hard time getting ready. Now my boss is giving me a hard time about being late and she's watching me like a hawk. I can see that I'm setting my kids off and I'm trying to not snap at them. And even thinking about being at work without more medication makes me feel worse."

Practitioner: "So one of the reasons this is so important now is that you are more anxious and more irritable than you were. You don't like the snowball effect those feelings are having on your kids, your schedule, and your work. You want to feel less anxious and irritable and you've been counting on the medication to help with that. It's hard to imagine managing your life without the medication."

Leona: "Yeah, I can't sleep, I feel anxious, and I panic. My hands shake, my heart pounds, I feel like I'm drowning, I can't think straight—it's terrifying. Everything is a constant battle. I'm tired all the time and I'm overwhelmed. I need more medication to be able to get some rest."

Practitioner: "Recently you've noticed that the irritability, anxiety, panic attacks, and trouble sleeping are getting worse. How have you been managing that?"

Leona: "I had to convince the doctor to increase my dose a while ago. She didn't want to, but eventually she did. Now she refuses to increase it again. She said the medication was just a 'temporary fix.' No offense, but I don't think meeting with you is going to help me."

Practitioner: "You've been managing a lot and I appreciate your willingness to talk with me. I want you to know, I'm not here to tell you that you have to make a change, but rather to work together with you to explore your goals and see what changes make sense to you."

Leona: "Well...frankly, I'm terrified. I know I've been on the medication for months and that wasn't the plan. But the truth is I really believe I need it more now. I'd prefer to revisit this taper when things are less stressful at work and I'm not having so much anxiety."

Practitioner: "So the medication helped at first but then your anxiety increased and you needed more to calm it. Now that you are on a higher dose, the anxiety is intensifying again. And that's making it hard to imagine how anything but increasing the dose is going to help."

Leona [tearing up]: "Exactly, the medication is the only thing that seems to work. I'm afraid to leave the house without it. It's been really hard."

ENGAGING

· · · · · ·

What skills does the practitioner use to engage with Leona and convey *empathy* and *understanding*?

_____

_____

_____

_____

_____

What does the practitioner say to indicate *partnering* with Leona?

_____

_____

_____

_____

_____

How do you think Leona feels after this conversation?

_____

_____

_____

_____

_____

OUR STRENGTHS IN ENGAGING

As practitioners, we bring a variety of strengths and skills to engaging people and building rapport. When we are *mindful* of our strengths and skills, our own authentic best selves come forward. People are more likely to engage with us when we are authentic—when we don't sound rehearsed or canned, when we don't rely on a script or set of stock questions. What are some of your strengths for engaging people?

- Are you warm, compassionate, and empathic?
- Are you a good listener? Accepting? Validating?
- Do you believe that people have the capacity and insight to change?
- Are you curious and interested in the capacities and insights that the people you work with bring to their lives?
- Are you optimistic for them?
- Do you help them explore solutions that they feel will best suit them?
- Do you enjoy positive outcomes in your sessions and services?

STRENGTHS FOR ENGAGING

· · · · · ·

What are your strengths for engaging with people?

_____

_____

_____

_____

_____

Please reflect on a recent conversation about change that went well.

_____

_____

_____

_____

_____

What skills did you use in that conversation? What strengths did you show the person?

_____

_____

_____

_____

_____

What was the encounter like? How did you support the person's exploration of their own situation, perception, and experiences? How did you support the person in bringing forward their own good ideas?

_____

_____

_____

_____

What do you think the person would have said about the encounter?

_____

_____

_____

_____

CHALLENGES OF ENGAGING

Engaging requires that we stay within the spirit of MI, which can be harder when the path to change is unclear. Conversations about change often explore more than changing just an attitude, skill, or routine. The person's exploration can bog down in self-doubt, shame, fear, reluctance, or refusal to change. Engaging is the safe space we establish before proceeding forward and the place we return to when we encounter reluctance or discord during the other processes (i.e., focusing, evoking, and planning).

Challenges to engaging people successfully can stem from the *context* of the service relationship, the *person* we serve, and/or us as *practitioners*. Challenges related to *context* can include:

- Engaging people in initial phone calls.
- Engaging people in teletherapy.
- Engaging people who may have had some prior unsatisfactory encounter with *our* services.
- Engaging people who have been court-mandated or otherwise compelled to attend our services.
- Engaging when our settings require certain behaviors that may impose barriers.

Challenges related to the *person* can include engaging people who:

- Are not yet really thinking about a change, or who are highly reluctant about change.
- Openly distrust helping professionals and/or service organizations generally.
- Don't feel well, are discouraged, are not sure that anything can really help their situation, or are overwhelmed by competing priorities.
- Have mental health issues that may hinder their ability to make connections.

Challenges related to the *practitioner* can include:

- Distracted listening.
- Telling a person that they ought to change, suggesting how they should go about it, or insisting that the change is really easy.
- Trying to impress upon the person the risks of not changing.
- Taking over the agenda, putting on our "fix-it hat," or any kind of non-mutuality that sends the signal "I know what's best for you."

BARRIERS TO ENGAGING

• • • • • •

Context

What additional *contextual* challenges can you think of?

_____

_____

_____

_____

Think of a recent contextual challenge you encountered. How did you manage it?

_____

_____

_____

_____

_____

The Person

What additional challenges related to *the person* can you think of?

_____

_____

_____

_____

_____

Think of a recent challenge related to a person with whom you are working. How did you manage it?

_____

_____

_____

_____

The Practitioner

What additional practitioner challenges can you think of?

_____

_____

_____

_____

Think of a recent challenge related to you as a practitioner. How did you manage it?

_____

_____

_____

_____

Barriers Posed by Our Work Settings

Often, expectations of our work settings present potential barriers to engaging. For example, organizations may require that practitioners conduct a comprehensive assessment before services begin, ask questions from a prescribed list, and provide specific information and recommendations during the initial intake. When practitioners use the first conversation to primarily ask fact-finding questions and conduct assessments, they evoke less information, less accurate information, and are less likely to engage the person in self-exploration and initiation of a change journey. However, there *are* MI-consistent ways to meet the needs of your organization and of the person with whom you are working.

MI-CONSISTENT WAYS TO GATHER ASSESSMENT INFORMATION

When we need to conduct an assessment or intake, we can wrap it in a brief 10-minute engaging conversation at the beginning and at the end. Ten minutes of MI-consistent conversation (or 20 percent of the conversation) develops rapport, increases the quality of the information gained, and increases the likelihood that the person will follow up on recommendations. We call this the "MI Sandwich," which can look something like:

> *"We need to accomplish some paperwork together today, and that will take about 30 minutes. Before we do that, I'd really like to take a few minutes to understand some of the things that are important to you, things on your mind. Then, we can complete the paperwork and we will have a few minutes to talk after that."*

From Checklist to Conversation

Collecting information or updating standard information (e.g., medication checks) can become a battery of closed questions. We want to avoid undermining rapport by interrogating the person or conveying that "my job is to ask and your job is to answer." We transform checklists using broad, open questions, reflections, and affirmations. We ask closed or follow-up questions as sparingly as possible. Some examples of broad open questions that might help with gathering checklist information include:

- "What are you already doing in this area of your life?"

- "What do you remember about what your doctor wanted you to do after your discharge? … Okay, there are some other things on the list, too. Is it alright if I share those with you?"

- "I'd like to check on your current medications before we talk about making any changes. Tell me about the medications you are currently taking—dosages, frequency, side effects, whatever you remember … Okay, there are some other meds on the list I have. I wonder if you would be willing to help me update the information on those, too, so the list is accurate?"

Consider the following two "takes" on an initial conversation with Samuel. In take one, the practitioner only asks questions. In take two, the practitioner uses the MI spirit and core skills to evoke the person's experiences, goals, readiness, and ideas for quitting smoking. What do you notice about the difference in rapport and Samuel's self-exploration of making the change?

Take One: The Practitioner Only Asks Questions

> The National Alliance on Mental Illness (n.d.) reports that 44.3 percent of all cigarettes are consumed by those with mental health issues.

Practitioner: "What brings you in today?"

Samuel: "I'd really like to stop smoking, but I don't know how."

Practitioner: "It sounds like you at least have some idea about what you want to change. Is there any reason behind that?"

Samuel: "I don't want to die."

Practitioner: "Okay, on a 1 to 10 scale—with 1 being not interested and 10 being very interested in change—where are you right now?"

Samuel: "My heart says I want to be at a 10, but my brain says I want cigarettes."

Practitioner: "So where would you be on that scale?"

Samuel: "I guess at about a 5."

Practitioner: "What makes you a 5 and not a 6?"

Samuel: "I recently gave it a good try and couldn't do it."

Practitioner: "So what are some strong things about you?"

Samuel: "I've been exercising, even though my chest burns and I get out of breath."

Practitioner: "So what are some other positive things that can help you achieve this goal?"

Samuel: "I don't like how people act when I smoke. Is that positive?"

Practitioner: "Well, there are no wrong answers. Have you actually attempted to quit smoking before?"

Samuel: "I tried nicotine patches and failed. I thought about trying medication, but I'm worried about side effects. So, I've been working out and trying to eat right, but it's not helping me quit smoking."

Practitioner: Change is scary…but do you want to cut down or quit?"

Samuel: "Pretty much."

Take Two: The Practitioner Works Toward Mutual Understanding While Guiding Toward Change

Practitioner: "Hi, Samuel. It's really good to meet you! So, what brings you in today?"

Samuel: "I'd really like to stop smoking, but I don't know how."

Practitioner: "You have good reasons to stop smoking."

Samuel: "I don't want to die."

Practitioner: "Your health is important to you, and quitting smoking is a part of that."

Samuel: "I've been trying to quit by exercising. I'm still working out, even though I don't like it and my chest burns and I get out of breath. I'm trying to lose weight, and I'm scared I'll just eat and gain weight if I stop smoking."

Practitioner: "This really is important to you; you're willing to be uncomfortable to reach your goal, and you're persisting with exercise even though you don't like it and it hurts when you're out of breath. That's not easy!"

Samuel: "Yeah, that's true. I wonder if there are other things I could try that would help me be successful? Maybe replace the cigarettes? I'm smoking about a pack per day."

Practitioner: "Well, there are lots of things that have helped people reduce their cigarettes per day and quit altogether. What do you already know about those?"

Samuel: "I've tried the patches, and those didn't work, and I'm scared of the medication's side effects. The only thing I can think of is eating more, and I don't want to do that. What are some other things people have done?"

Practitioner: "There are a number of things people do to reduce and quit altogether. One thing people do is remove some of the cigarettes in their pack so they only smoke the cigarettes in the pack—like if they are smoking 20 a day, they'll take 5 out to reduce it to 15 a day. Another thing people do is to change a trigger for their smoking. For example, if they smoke their first cigarette of the day with their cup of morning coffee, they'll switch from coffee to tea or orange juice in the morning. A third thing people will do is take a walk whenever they take a break during the day instead of smoking. And people sometimes keep their cigarettes somewhere inconvenient, like the trunk of their car, so they aren't tempted to smoke while driving. What do you think about those ideas? It's your decision what you do to reduce your smoking and eventually quit."

Samuel: "Well, I do smoke first thing with coffee, and in the car, and on my breaks. I could try that idea of removing five cigarettes from the pack to begin reducing my use and putting the pack in the trunk of my car, so I don't smoke when I'm driving."

Practitioner: "That sounds like a manageable first step to you. What else?"

Samuel: "I think I'd like to see how I do with that and then talk about what I might do next."

Practitioner: "Let me just summarize where we're at here and see if I understand. Reducing your cigarettes per day sounds like something you'd like to try, and you'd like to start by taking five cigarettes out of the pack and keeping the pack in the trunk of your car. You're worried about the effects of smoking on your health and committed to making some changes. This seems like a manageable first step. Is that about right?"

Samuel: "Yes. I want to try this and see if I can cut down. I'm hoping it will help me quit."

Practitioner: "You see a connection for you between cutting down and quitting."

Samuel: "Yes. I might be able to use the patches after I cut down, but I want to see how this goes first."

Practitioner: "Okay, it sounds like you have a preliminary plan here of removing five cigarettes from your pack each day and keeping the pack in the trunk of your car. What thoughts do you have about what might help you be successful with this plan?"

TWO TAKES: CONVERSATIONS ABOUT QUITTING SMOKING

• • • • • •

Now that you have read both take one and take two:

How is the practitioner's attitude and style different in take one compared to take two?

_____

_____

_____

_____

What effect does this difference seem to have on *engaging* Samuel into a conversation about quitting smoking in take one?

_____

_____

_____

_____

In take two?

_____

_____

_____

_____

_____

How are Samuel's signals about his interest in exploring quitting smoking different in take one compared to take two?

_____

_____

_____

_____

_____

What *core skills* does the practitioner use in take two that help Samuel gain access to his own wisdom, experience, choice, and intrinsic motivation?

_____

_____

_____

_____

_____

Exploring Past Treatment Experiences

During engaging we work to understand the person's perception and past experience with treatment. As we explore the events that brought the person in to talk with us and their perception of the need for change, we also want to explore past treatment experiences and how those were related to the person's management of their condition and their follow-through—or lack thereof—with treatment and between-session activities. We can gain important information like:

- "I don't think the medications did anything for me except make me too sleepy. I stopped taking them."
- "I took the medication, but I was still depressed."
- "I don't think my clinician really cared about me."

Typical Day Format

Asking about a person's typical day is a collaborative and engaging way to conduct a comprehensive assessment in a short period of time. It is helpful to start with a transparent intention (Undrill & Toogood, 2018):

> *"We have a long assessment to complete. But rather than ask you a lot of questions, most people find it easier to start by talking about a recent day—a day that was like any other day. That will answer a lot of the questions and help us see a picture together of what life looks like for you. I'll probably still need to ask some follow-up questions at the end, to fill in the gaps and find out more about how [substance use or other topic] fits into your daily life. What do you think of that? Does it sound alright to start with a typical day for you?"*

We can offer reflections, affirmations, and clarifying open questions to keep the narrative moving in a productive direction. Periodic summarizing can help ensure that we have an accurate understanding of what the person is telling us about their life.

ENGAGING WITH OPEN QUESTIONS, AFFIRMATIONS, AND REFLECTIONS

Engaging with Open Questions

Wide open, collaborative, compassionate, and evocative questions offer alternatives to fact-finding questions and give the person freedom in choosing how to respond. As noted in Chapter 4, people tend to offer more complete and accurate information in response to open and collaborative questions than in response to closed fact-finding questions (Robinson & Heritage, 2006)

The Harvesting Hopes tool provides a strong start to engaging and guiding forward with open and collaborative questions. It can be used to explore a person's own expectations for services, hopes for outcomes, and optimal circumstances for flourishing. Many people find creative activities helpful for viewing information from a fresh perspective. These activities can increase insight and connections among concepts, cognitive flexibility, and new ideas (Birgilli, 2015; Chan, 2013).

HARVESTING HOPES

• • • • • •

Preparation

You will need:

- A good-sized piece of paper on which to draw a picture of a tree.

- Different colored markers or pencils. Sticky notes can also be handy.

- Either sketch the tree yourself or invite the person to sketch the tree because it will be *their* tree for harvesting *their* hopes. Some roots, a trunk, and some branches are sufficient detail. Allow enough space on the paper for the person to write their insights and ideas on the tree and all around it.

Introducing the Activity

You might start by saying something like:

"As we begin working together, I am curious about what hopes you bring to our conversation. I would also love to know what kind of skills and knowledge you have that will support our work, and what would help you feel comfortable working together. If you are willing, we can use this space to draw a tree and explore your ideas about harvesting your hopes. We find that this activity can help people explore their ideas even more deeply and make connections that help them decide what to do next. It's up to you if you want to do this or not. If you are willing, one of us, either me or you, will draw a tree. It doesn't have to look perfect—just a trunk, some roots, and some branches will help us explore your hopes, comfort, skills, and knowledge for our work together. I will offer some specific questions that may guide your exploration a bit. It's ultimately your choice how you use this activity."

Gathering the Harvest: Examples of Open and Collaborative Questions to Guide Exploration

- "What are the hoped-for outcomes that you have for our work together? You could think of these as fruits that you'd draw on the branches."

- "What are your strengths and skills that you want to bring to our work? You could think of these as resources that will support and nourish your efforts. Maybe you could draw these on the tree trunk or in the surrounding grasses."

- "What are some of the conditions that would help support our work together? For example, what would you like from me? Or what would you like from those closest to you? You might draw these in the air, under the roots, or anywhere else that you'd like."

- "Okay, nicely done. Now, tell me about what you see here. How would you describe your picture to someone else?"

Engaging with Affirmations

Affirmations are a powerful skill for establishing rapport especially when people have a lived experience of serious mental health issues. One activity that can help people identify and appreciate their strengths and skills uses the Strengths of Successful Changers tool introduced in Chapter 4.

Engaging with Reflections

Reflective listening skills are the backbone of the engaging process. Frequent, accurate reflections convey our interest in and respect for what the person is saying. To reflect and engage well, we:

- Listen carefully, without judgment and interruption, for the person's thoughts, beliefs, and feelings.
- Pay particular attention to reflecting the person's thoughts and feelings related to:
    - Their values, goals, and intentions.
    - Their strengths, skills, and resources.
    - The barriers they perceive to achieving their goals.
    - How health, mental health, substance use, or other issues might be posing barriers to their goals.

People appreciate the opportunity to think through the important issues in their lives with someone who is listening well. Listening well is the foundation of an effective conversation about change. When people feel reluctant to talk to us or have difficulty putting their experience into words, reflections are helpful ways to communicate interest, acceptance, and compassion. We can tentatively reflect what we think the person's experience may be based on their affect and appearance. Our efforts to understand when the person is struggling to communicate help us establish our intention to work together and create a safe space for our work together.

USING THE STRENGTHS OF SUCCESSFUL CHANGERS TOOL

• • • • • •

Place the Strengths of Successful Changers tool on the table between you and the person. Ask the person to identify three or more of their skills, strengths, capacities, and positive qualities.

- Invite them to write down or discuss what they value about these qualities and how they use these qualities in their life or in specific situations (e.g., to achieve past successes or overcome current challenges). Affirm their strengths, skills, efforts, and intentions.

- Ask the person to identify two or three of their most strongly held values. Invite them to write down or discuss what those values mean to them. Then, have them identify how the strengths they identified from the Strengths of Successful Changers tool help them to act consistently with their values. Affirm their strengths, skills, efforts, and intentions.

- Ask the person to imagine saying: "A year from now, I'm going to be glad I got started on [this change] today." Reflect the change and ask about one thing the person could do to set it in motion right away. Reflect or affirm their response, such as "I know this has been difficult for you and you have really shown determination here."

- Ask the person to identify some skills or strengths from the Strengths of Successful Changers tool that they would like to cultivate in their lives and identify ways they can begin doing that. Reflect or affirm their response.

REFLECTING TO CREATE A SAFE SPACE

· · · · · ·

Scenario 1

Imagine sitting with someone who is tense and silent. What might you say to them to communicate interest and compassion? What might you reflect?

_____

_____

_____

_____

_____

Practitioner [example]: "I'm interested in hearing from you how you are. My sense is that this is a hard day for you—you seem to be feeling a lot of pain."

How might the person respond?

_____

_____

_____

_____

_____

What might you say next to help the person keep talking about their experience?

_____

_____

_____

_____

_____

Now imagine that *you* are the person and you are thinking: "I want to die. I can't stand feeling this way. If I open my mouth, I'll scream." Consider your practitioner responses. How would you as the person feel about talking to you as the practitioner? How safe, interested, and compassionate does the practitioner seem?

_____

_____

_____

_____

_____

What makes your reflections work in this conversation?

_____

_____

_____

_____

_____

How might you change your reflections to make them even safer and more compassionate?

_____

_____

_____

_____

_____

Scenario 2

Imagine sitting with someone who is sleepy, almost snoring, breathing deeply. What might you say to signal interest? What might you reflect?

_____

_____

_____

_____

_____

Practitioner [example]: "I'm interested in hearing how it's been for you. It looks like you are exhausted; it seems like it's hard for you to keep your eyes open right now. It must have been hard to come here when you are feeling this tired." How might the person respond?

_____

_____

_____

_____

What might you say next to help the person keep talking about their experience?

_____

_____

_____

_____

Imagine that *you* are the person and you are thinking: "This is hopeless, there is nothing I can do. I am alone. No one is going to help." Consider your practitioner responses. How would you as the person feel about talking to you as the practitioner? How safe, interested, and compassionate does the practitioner seem?

_____

_____

_____

_____

_____

What makes your reflections work in this conversation?

_____

_____

_____

_____

How might you change your reflections to make them even safer and more compassionate?

_____

_____

_____

_____

Listening Reflectively with Metaphors

Metaphors are a powerful way to show someone we are understanding their experience and perception. When we offer a metaphor that captures a person's *meaning*, it feels to them that we really "get it," and encourages their further self-exploration. It is important to use metaphors that are appropriate to the person's culture and tailored to the person's individual identity, strengths, and values. The following are some examples of metaphors that can be adapted to capture a variety of experiences people describe in conversations about change. For example, when a person is facing a challenging set of circumstances, we might say something like:

- "This really seems like a big mountain to you."
- "It's all tangled up right now."
- "You've got the weight of the world on your shoulders right now."
- "It's been an uphill climb so far."
- "This has been a real roller-coaster ride for you."

When a person is facing a dilemma with unpleasant options, we might say something like:

- "It feels like you're caught between a rock and a hard place."
- "It's like jumping from the frying pan into the fire."

When a person is facing several desirable options, we might say something like:

- "It's like you're a kid in a candy store."
- "It's like having your cake and eating it too."

When a person is facing a momentous decision, we might say something like:

- "You're at a real turning point."
- "You find yourself at a fork in the road."
- "You're really torn about this."

When a person has made a difficult decision or initiated a plan, we might say something like:

- "It feels like you're nearly home free."
- "You're circling the bases and heading for home plate."
- "It all seems downhill from here."
- "With all you've put in place, it's like you've hit the jackpot now."

REFLECTING WITH METAPHORS

· · · · · ·

What are some metaphors you have already used to show a person that you understand them?

_____

_____

_____

_____

_____

What are some others you think might be useful?

_____

_____

_____

_____

_____

ENGAGING BY EXPLORING VALUES AND PRIORITIES

Our values are related to our intrinsic motivation, aspirations, and goals. We grow and develop in directions that are consistent with what we most care about. Exploring values with compassion and appreciation clarifies where we are and where we want to be. Values exploration builds trust and rapport. It sets the stage for discovery and identifying meaningful life goals. Exploring a person's priorities and values using reflections elevates the person's sense of *being seen* and helps to harness their considerable strengths. For example:

- "You mentioned that _____ is very important to you. What are some examples of ways you already have _____ in your life?"
- "What might we work on together to help you have _____ in your life even more?"

The Values Grid

The Values Grid is a useful tool that supports exploring a person's most important values. This tool can be adapted to reflect the values of the populations you serve.

THE VALUES GRID

• • • • • •

Acceptance *To be accepted as I am*	Achievement *To have important accomplishments*	Caring *To take care of others*	Change *To have a life full of change and variety*	Comfort *To have a pleasant and comfortable life*	Compassion *To feel and act on concern for others*
Contribution *To make a lasting contribution in the world*	Dependability *To be reliable and trustworthy*	Ecology *To live in harmony with the environment*	Excitement *To have a life full of thrills and stimulation*	Family *To have a happy, loving family*	Fitness *To be physically fit and strong*
Friendship *To have close, supportive friends*	Fun *To play and have fun*	God's will *To seek and obey the will of God*	Growth *To keep changing and growing*	Health *To be physically well and healthy*	Hope *To maintain a positive and optimistic outlook*
Independence *To be free from dependence on others*	Knowledge *To learn and contribute valuable knowledge*	Love *To be loved and give love to others*	Moderation *To avoid excesses and find a middle ground*	Nonconformity *To question authority and challenge norms*	Pleasure *To feel good*
Purpose *To have meaning and direction in my life*	Responsibility *To make and carry out responsible decisions*	Safety *To be safe and secure*	Self-Acceptance *To accept myself as I am*	Self-Knowledge *To have a deep and honest understanding of myself*	Wealth *To have plenty of money*

Adapted from: Miller, C'de Baca, Matthews, & Wilbourne, 2001.

USING THE VALUES GRID

• • • • • •

To introduce the Values Grid exercise, you might say something like: "This is a list of values that people often hold as important. As you look at this table, what three values are important to you in your life?"

Guide the person's self-exploration with open questions about each value they identify, like:

"Tell me more about why this value is important to you."

"In the last month or so, what are some things that you have been doing that support this value?"

"How is this value related to the change(s) you are considering?"

Use frequent reflections and affirmations and summarize your understanding of the person's values and how the values relate to the person's identified or potential change focus(es) and potential next steps.

Values Card Sort

We also can use a *card sort* to explore a person's values and priorities. For the card sort exercise the values are written on individual cards or slips of paper. Miller and colleagues (2001) suggest having the person go through the cards and sort them into categories: important to me, very important to me, and not important to me. The practitioner guides the discussion as with the values grid. A template of cards is available at tinyurl.com/4uadfqht.

Adapting Values Tools

It is important to be flexible in adapting discussions about values to be sure that our conversations are as relevant to the person as possible. We might choose to collaborate with the person to create from scratch a values grid that is more relevant to them. Or we can adapt the values grid or card sort exercises for a particular population.

When working with a young person we may want to add things like:

- Getting good grades.
- Peace in my family.
- Being independent.
- Being seen as "cool" by my peers.
- Getting into college.

Note: A card sort template for teen values is at tinyurl.com/4rsbwxtj.

When working with a person who is homeless, we could add things like:

- People I can trust.
- Money in my pocket.
- A safe place to sleep.
- Freedom from troubling thoughts.
- A cup of coffee and a meal.
- Time with my kids.

For people who experience symptoms of thought disorders, Moyers and Martino (2006) modified the values card sort activity by removing abstract concepts and adding in relevant goals and values (e.g., medications that work for me, not hearing voices, feel like I fit in). The adapted card sort and instructions are available on the MINT website: tinyurl.com/15926daf.

Exploring Values and Wisdom in Unusual Choices

Sometimes a behavior that does not seem to make sense on the surface has underlying value and wisdom. Questioning the person's behavior can make the person feel disrespected, rejected, and misunderstood. Acceptance and exploration of the *function* of the person's behavior can help to reveal deeply held values and wise choices. Honoring the person's values and wisdom makes it easier for the person to consider other pathways toward their goals. Consider Maria:

Maria has lived on the streets most of her life. She recently made a decision to enter residential treatment to give herself a bit of a break. There she saw others talking together and wanted to be a part of things. This surprised her, because connecting with others was not of primary importance to her on the street. But in watching others, she felt a little left out and wanted to be part of it.

The other people were horrified when Maria tried to connect with them—they told her that her hygiene was bad and that she needed to clean up if she wanted to hang out with them. This was painful for her, and the more they confronted her the worse her hygiene habits became. The treatment practitioner knew a little about MI and asked to talk with Maria about her important values, thinking that a values clarification activity might help them work together for what mattered to Maria.

Maria said that safety was her most important value. On the streets if she didn't shower or change her clothes people would leave her alone and she could feel safe. Much to her surprise, she now wanted to talk with people, and the strategy that had kept her safe was now a wedge. The practitioner honored Maria's value to stay safe and reflected that what had worked so well for her was now having a different result. The practitioner wondered whether Maria had thought of other ways to stay safe that would allow her to make some shifts from what had been helpful on the street.

Maria said she was not sure about it but had heard there were some classes at the facility where she could learn to talk to others, set boundaries, and decide whether to place trust in others. Maria was describing some interpersonal effectiveness skill-building classes. The practitioner asked if she would be interested in trying the classes and what she hoped she could get out of them. Maria thought that being able to set boundaries with her words would help her move beyond the ways that had worked for her on the streets and were now causing pain. She decided to give it a try, and she was able to make some changes in how she kept herself safe, increasing her sense of self-efficacy and allowing for more connection with others.

PREPARING FOR ENGAGING CONVERSATIONS

Effective engagement starts with our readiness to understand and honor the person's perception, experiences, goals, and readiness for change. We can prepare to engage effectively by focusing our intentions to support and maintain the person's trust through compassion, accurate understanding, and respectful services.

The amount of time the practitioner might devote specifically to the process of engaging depends on many factors. A good general guideline is to plan to spend about 20 percent of the total conversation in the engaging process (e.g., 1 minute of a 5-minute conversation, 5 minutes of a 25-minute conversation). And then, when we guide through focusing, evoking, and planning, we continue to use an engaging style and return to the process of engaging when needed.

We can open up opportunities to engage and guide toward changes the person wants to make, and ultimately increase the effectiveness of our services through simple shifts in our skills, such as:

- Listening more.
- Expressing interest in the person's priorities, goals, and expectations.
- Affirming their strengths, skills, and values.

The following exercise can help you think about preparing to engage and reflect on your engagement outcomes.

PREPARING TO ENGAGE

· · · · · ·

Consider a person currently participating in your services.

How might you prepare *before* your next conversation about change to be ready to listen and be curious about the person's experience, goals, and expectations?

_____

_____

_____

How might you make the time to listen and be curious about the person's experience, goals, and expectations in your next conversation about change?

_____

_____

_____

How might you use more reflections, affirmations, and summaries—and fewer questions?

_____

_____

_____

How might you increase collaboration and the person's options for making a change and emphasize the person's autonomy in deciding what will work best for them?

_____

_____

_____

ONGOING ASSESSMENT OF OUR ABILITY TO ENGAGE

The people with whom we work are experts on how we can more effectively engage them. To increase our skills, we can ask them to respond to some simple questions about their experience of our conversation at the end of each session. We explore their answers using excellent listening and partnering skills to understand how we can better engage them in our services. Their feedback informs our practice and contributes to our own professional development. This practitioner tool offers a structure for obtaining feedback from those with whom we work.

ASSESSING ABILITY TO ENGAGE

• • • • • •

Ask the person (or provide a hard copy of this): On a scale from 1 to 10, with 1 being "not at all" and 10 being "excellent":

- How well did I pay attention to your priorities today?

- How welcomed, valued, and accepted did you feel?

- How well did this experience live up to your expectations?

- How well did this conversation support your progress toward your goals?

The following exercise explores what you are already doing to engage and support a person's self-exploration. You can also begin to identify the skill areas you want to strengthen to enhance the engaging process.

REFLECTING ON OUR ENGAGING OUTCOMES

· · · · · ·

Think about a recent conversation about change that went well (or less well, your choice). You may want to listen to a recording of a session to refresh your memory.

What personal problems did the person explore with you?

_____

_____

_____

_____

_____

How did the person describe themselves to you? What did they reveal about their inner perceptions and experiences to you?

_____

_____

_____

_____

_____

What personally relevant material did the person reveal to you that demonstrated their sense of safety with you?

_____

_____

_____

_____

_____

What did you do to support their self-exploration and sense of safety in sharing this with you?

_____

_____

_____

_____

_____

What personal values or life choices did the person share with you (e.g., what is most important to them, what values guide their decisions)?

_____

_____

_____

_____

_____

What did you do to support their self-exploration and sense of safety in sharing this with you?

_____

_____

_____

_____

_____

How does the person feel about their current situation? What is their perspective?

_____

_____

_____

_____

_____

What are the person's roles and responsibilities to others and to themselves? How did the person describe their roles and responsibilities?

_____

_____

_____

_____

_____

What did the person say about their skills, strengths, abilities, capacities, and efforts?

_____

_____

_____

_____

_____

What is the person's sense of their own self-worth?

_____

_____

_____

_____

_____

How did the person's self-exploration of these areas evolve or deepen over the course of your conversation?

_____

_____

_____

_____

_____

How did you listen deeply and develop your mutual understanding of the person's situation and goals *beyond* what they said?

_____

_____

_____

_____

_____

THE DANCE OF MI: INTRODUCTION TO A FRAMEWORK

It is sometimes hard to imagine what guiding a conversation through the four processes might look like. Here is a basic "dance of MI" framework for guiding a conversation from one process to another. We will use this framework at the end of each process chapter. The framework includes:

- Signals to increase [the current process].
- Practitioner strategies to increase [the current process].
- Signals to guide toward [the next process].
- Practitioner strategies to guide toward [the next process].

Although this framework shows a fairly straight progression from process to process, it is important to remember that the dance of MI can move in any direction. Sometimes the conversation must move back to an earlier process before continuing forward.

THE DANCE OF MI: MOVING FROM ENGAGING TO FOCUSING

Our goal for the engaging process is to develop a rapport that allows us to help the person consider and begin to work toward effective self-management activities. As they begin to consider a potential change direction, we shift into the focusing process and identifying a specific, mutually determined, change focus.

Signals to Increase Engaging

- The person seems uncomfortable.
- The conversation is unpleasant or rough.
- The person appears to be passive, withdrawn, stuck, or rebellious.
- The person talks more about *not* making a change than about making a change.

Practitioner Strategies to Increase Engaging

When the going gets rough, try these strategies to engage, reengage, and increase partnering and acceptance:

- Seek to understand the person's perspective, priorities, and dilemma primarily using reflections and summaries. When asking questions, aim for evocative questions filled with gentle interest.
- Seek collaboration: Evoke and follow the person's priorities at least as much as your own: "What would you like to talk about today?" "What would you like us to work on together?"
- Emphasize autonomy and the person's right to choose: "You know yourself best here, what do *you* think you need to do?" "What makes the most sense for you?"
- Affirm the person's values, strengths, wisdom, and intentions based on what they've already said.

- Offer general information about the potential change focus(es) and possible options for change in an MI-consistent way.
- Avoid using persuasion, confrontation, too many questions, and offering unsolicited advice, information, and suggestions.

Signals to Guide Toward Focusing

- The person seems comfortable.
- The person is doing most of the talking, exploring the changes they might want to make and correcting any inaccurate understandings.
- The person has identified a change focus or expressed interest in identifying a change focus.

Practitioner Strategies to Guide Toward Focusing

- Check accurate understanding by summarizing what the person wants and their perceived dilemmas or barriers.
- Reflect emerging focus(es) from the person's perspective or ask about where they want to focus.
- If the person expresses limited options for change focus, offer choices for how to proceed (e.g., a menu of options).

CHAPTER SUMMARY

· · · · · ·

What do you see as the most important points of this chapter?

_____

_____

_____

_____

What interested you the most?

_____

_____

_____

_____

What engagement strategies would you most like to try, or work on improving?

_____

_____

_____

_____

6

FOCUSING: THE STRATEGIC DIRECTION

The path out of ambivalence is to choose a direction and follow it,
to keep moving in the chosen direction.

—Miller & Rollnick, 2013, p. 7

IN THIS CHAPTER

- Straightforward Focusing
- Shared Agenda Focusing
- Sorting Multiple Potential Change Focuses
- Focusing When the Focus Is Unclear
- Tools to Help Identify and Prioritize Focuses
- The Dance of MI: Moving from Focusing to Evoking

Focusing is developing and maintaining a specific direction in a conversation about change. The focusing process follows and builds on the engaging process. The partnership, empathy, and acceptance established in engaging lay the foundation for focusing. Focusing is essential to evoking and planning.

In focusing we explore the person's priorities and agenda for change and how they relate to their larger life goals. We explore the dilemmas that interfere with the change (e.g., symptom management, basic needs, social support) and avoid pressing against the person's preferences (e.g., treatment engagement, medication adherence, behavior change, between-session activities). Instead we work to balance the person's agenda with our own, further developing the working alliance and identifying areas of mutual agreement. This process reduces the person's experience of isolation, potential for dissonance, and reluctance to explore healthy change options.

Focusing is a complex skill. Our ability to focus well significantly impacts the outcomes of our change conversations. When there is a wobbly or unclear focus, the conversation might slip and slide without making much progress. A focus that lacks meaning or isn't a priority for the person (i.e., one that is solely our agenda) results in poorer outcomes.

Developing a clear direction and focus for change supports the person's ability to explore whether and why they might make the change (i.e., evoking). In this chapter, we will present different ways to develop, maintain, and restore focus, as well as tools to help prioritize focuses when there are multiple options, and move from focusing to evoking.

STRAIGHTFORWARD FOCUSING

Focusing is sometimes straightforward; for example, when someone is already thinking about making a change (e.g., with regard to smoking cessation, substance use, nutrition, medication). They may already have some ideas about what will work for them, or there may be a range of options that we can explore with them about making the change: "I hear that x is your top priority. How can I be helpful as we work together on this?"

SHARED AGENDA FOCUSING

Focusing is often based on both what the person came to talk about—their ultimate goal—and what the practitioner sees as important to explore. Certain change focuses are more difficult to develop than others. For example, it is challenging to develop medication adherence as a change focus with someone who has expressed a desire to *not* take medications. It can be helpful to explore the person's priorities *first* while transparently setting aside time to explore other focuses as well:

- "I'm sure you have some priorities today. Let's get to those first, and before you go, I want to look at a couple of things together as well."

- "Today we have about thirty minutes. Let's take the first part of our time together to talk about your top priority, and before you go, I'd like to explore a couple of other things with you."

- "I have some things that I would like to address with you, so let's save some time for that at the end, but first, let's talk about what's most important to you to address today."

Similarly, some focuses are sensitive given the person's circumstances (e.g., substance use with a woman who is pregnant, weight loss with a person who is obese, sexually transmitted diseases with a person in a committed relationship). In these situations, we can offer a menu of options so the person can choose where to start. Here are two examples:

Person: "I can't stop, this is what helps me calm down, this is what gets me through the day, and besides, everyone has something they do to manage their stress."

Practitioner: "It's hard to imagine how your life could be different. That's a common concern for people who are uncertain about quitting smoking. If you are interested, there are a number of things we could talk about that have helped people in similar situations. One place we could start involves the stress in your life and some additional ways people manage stress. Another topic is the small steps people have found helpful to get ready to stop, things that build their interest and confidence for stopping. I wonder if any of those topics seem helpful to you, or perhaps there's something else you'd rather talk about?"

Practitioner: "Hi, Jim. I understand that you were asked to come in to see me because of an accident at work. In order for us to work together, we'll need to explore some areas related to that, but we don't have to start there. We can get to those topics after we've talked about your concerns about being here and what's most important to you."

Switching Focus

Sharing the agenda can also occur when we need to switch focuses because of unanticipated events or because we have additional focuses we need to address. In these situations, we want to maintain the relational foundation we've established while also proposing the new focus. It is important that we not push our ideas onto the person or offer "expert" advice. Rather, we summarize our progress on the earlier focus and then ask permission to transparently transition to the new change focus:

- "And now, if it's alright with you, perhaps we could talk about your smoking?"
- "Let's turn now to the range of options for participating in this program. I'm interested in your thoughts about these. It's ultimately your decision what you do with this information and whether you decide to participate."

Another option for transparently changing the focus is to engage and focus on the person's priorities first and ask about the next change focus when it comes up naturally. We continue using empathy and autonomy support skills to address any potential discord that may arise:

- "As I'm listening to you, I'm wondering about how getting mad might be related to the experience you're describing. Would you be willing to talk some about what that was like for you?"
- "Now that we've addressed the medication issue, I wonder if you'd be willing to talk some about the group?"

Sometimes, asking permission is inappropriate—for example, it is not optional to inform someone of the conditions of their probation or to tell someone the results of their lab tests. In these instances, emphasizing the person's autonomy (i.e., that it is their choice to decide what to *do* with the information) can help to preserve the rapport we've worked to develop.

SHARING THE FOCUS OF CHANGE

• • • • • •

Think about a recent change conversation you had with someone where the focus of change needed to be shared (i.e., you and the person had different focuses to discuss).

What are you already doing in order to ensure that you develop a mutually agreed on change focus that incorporates both their agenda and yours?

_____

_____

_____

What skills did you use to ensure that you sustained partnering as you negotiated the shared focus of change?

_____

_____

_____

How did you feel about the outcome of this recent conversation?

_____

_____

_____

Is there anything you might want to do differently in a similar situation?

_____

_____

_____

SORTING MULTIPLE POTENTIAL CHANGE FOCUSES

When multiple change focuses need to be addressed, the initial challenge is to support the person in prioritizing their change focus *for that conversation*. For example:

> *There are a number of things that we typically discuss with people who are looking to find housing: specific housing requirements, access to transportation, concerns about safety, and anything that has interfered with maintaining housing in the past. I'm wondering what is at the top of your list? Where would you like to start?*

The people we serve commonly experience co-occurring mental health issues, and they may shift from focus to focus in the same conversation. For example, during a conversation with a person experiencing symptoms of depression, we may also discover some significant issues related to alcohol use. We can transparently refocus the conversation to explore the person's alcohol use and how it is related to managing their depression. This relationship between alcohol and depression can be a large umbrella topic consisting of multiple potential focuses, such as the impact of their alcohol use on their depression, their strengths and skills for managing depression without alcohol, etc. A bubble sheet (see Agenda Maps later in this chapter) is a helpful way to transparently set an agenda for the conversation and navigate interrelated focuses.

Flexibly navigating interrelated focuses supports the person's autonomy and intrinsic motivation to make a change. A person who is homeless may see obtaining housing as a simple goal, while the practitioner knows that a number of other issues may need to be addressed along the way to ensure success (e.g., housing applications, ambivalence about moving into an unfamiliar environment, budgeting, job or disability payments, and management of health, mental health, and/or addiction issues that may interfere with maintaining housing). The practitioner works with the person's primary goal (e.g., housing first) and looks for opportunities to address other related issues as they emerge and as the person is willing. These conversations about multiple changes could span weeks or months as the person and practitioner navigate trust building (engaging), focusing (and refocusing), evoking (for each focus as it emerges), and planning appropriate to the person's readiness.

Focusing and Ambivalence

People who experience co-occurring issues sometimes shift from focus to focus in the same conversation to manage their ambivalence about making a change. It can be helpful to follow the person's lead on a new issue and, as they are ready, tie together the new focus and the original focus (i.e., understand the underlying connection or dilemma). Working together to decide whether to continue with the original focus or shift to the new focus helps people feel safe exploring the connections between co-occurring issues. A bubble sheet (see Agenda Maps later in this chapter) is a helpful way to keep track of these new focuses and underlying connections.

We respond to ambivalence or reluctance about change focuses like substance use, medications, sleep routines, etc. with interest and curiosity. When the person is set against talking about a change focus that we think is a good idea, we respond by normalizing and understanding their stance, supporting their autonomy, and shifting the conversation to another focus. As the alliance develops, the person may become more willing to explore the focus that was initially unacceptable.

When the person's ambivalence about addressing a particular change focus is strong, we can tailor evocation and planning to increase the person's awareness of the impact of their current behavior on their goals and values, and discovery of others' experiences with the behavior change (e.g., medication and treatment, etc.).

Focusing and Exploring Values and Strengths

Values and strengths exploration can be used during focusing to increase a person's willingness to identify and prioritize change focuses. A return or introduction to the Values Grid or values card sort tools, and Strengths of Successful Changers tool (introduced in Chapter 5) can be particularly helpful in focusing. Highlighting the person's strengths and resources increases their confidence for managing distressing experiences and resolving basic needs. Exploring how a change focus is related to a person's needs in the short and the long term also helps them move beyond compliance-only efforts and into sustainable behavior change consistent with their values and strengths. For example:

- "How might that help you now and in the future?"
- "What, for you, might be the best possible things to come out of your successes here?"
- "While I can understand it's not the top of your list right now, I do hear for you that temporarily making some changes with your drinking can help you get this behind you— that sounds most important to you."
- "I get this is low on your list. We can talk about it another time. What might be more important for us to talk about today?"

Let's revisit Leona (from Chapter 5). Her situation is an example of shared focus. Her physician has referred her to the practitioner because they believe she has developed a tolerance to alprazolam and needs to taper off the medication. Leona, however, is extremely ambivalent about focusing on this change and is highly concerned with her anxiety and panic, and her ability to make it through her days.

Practitioner [evoking strengths to reduce ambivalence about exploring a potential taper]: "You've mentioned that you try to keep the medication with you at all times. Tell me about a time when you had to delay a dose. What was that like for you?"

Leona: "Well, I got like these waves of intense anxiety, my hands were shaking, I felt sick…"

Practitioner: "You went through a lot tolerating that. How did you manage between the time the waves of anxiety started and when you took the medication?"

Leona: "Wow, that wasn't easy. I tried to distract myself, but I couldn't concentrate, it was really hard."

Practitioner: "You were pretty uncomfortable and tried distracting yourself. It sounds like you made it through even though it felt pretty intolerable. Like you were white-knuckling it all the way."

Leona: "Yeah, and it really is worse now than it's ever been. Maybe you could help me convince the doctor that I need to go up on the dose first and then when I'm better we can talk about a taper."

Practitioner [shifting the focus from the taper to increasing awareness of the relationship between anxiety and a dose increase]: "Well, I'm hearing that you get some relief when you increase the dose. I'm also hearing that even on the increased dose the anxiety and panic seem to get worse again. I'm wondering if we could talk about what you already know about what causes the anxiety to increase even on the higher medication dose?"

Leona: "Ummm... I think I talked to the doctor about that, but I don't really remember what she said."

Practitioner: "So for some people, they never feel the need to increase the dose. And for others, they develop what's called a 'tolerance' to the medication. That means the brain adjusts to the medication and counteracts its effect. Some people experience intense anxiety, irritation, and insomnia as a result even though they are still taking the medication. People often feel they need more medication to feel calm and in control, and then the cycle starts again. It sounds like that may be what is happening in your situation. How does that fit with your experience?"

Leona: "The medication is the only thing that works, and now you're saying tolerance is the reason my anxiety is worse. Why not just increase my dose?"

Practitioner: "That's a really good question. So, the medication isn't intended for long-term use because it has side effects like problems with memory, concentration, fatigue, and coordination. Longer term use and higher doses can cause those effects to persist even after the medication is stopped. What thoughts do you have about that?"

Leona: "I have noticed that it makes me feel fuzzy and kind of weird, like disconnected from things, and I'm pretty tired most the time, but I do a lot, you know? And my life is hard."

Practitioner [reinforcing awareness of the experiences she's having and the dose]: "So it makes sense to you that the medication might be at least in part responsible for some of the recent things you've been experiencing: the fuzziness and feeling disconnected and tired."

Leona [signaling a willingness to refocus on the taper]: "Are you saying that even if I stop the medication now, because my dose was increased, that stuff will continue?"

Practitioner [focusing on the taper]: "Not necessarily, people are all different—most people quitting the medication experience a brief increase in their anxiety levels. Others might feel the effects on and off for a while. Things like being nervous, jumpy, on-edge, depressed, trouble sleeping. It's not that pleasant, but millions of people successfully quit with a taper and go on to live even happier lives with a lot more confidence for managing their anxiety."

Leona: "I like the sound of confidence for managing my anxiety, but do the people who quit have anxiety *and* panic attacks? It's not like I'm using the medication for the experience. I actually need the relief. Sometimes it feels like I'm going crazy or I might die. It gets bad."

Practitioner [reinforcing her interest in increasing her ability to manage her anxiety and supporting autonomy]: "Concern about losing control over the anxiety is really common, and it makes a lot of sense given everything you've been dealing with. You've been doing your best to manage a hard situation, and people do learn how to manage these experiences with more confidence. It's really your choice what you do with this information. If you want, we can work together with your doctor to find a way that works for you to get off this roller-coaster of anxiety, panic, irritation, and trouble sleeping."

Leona: "Well, I see how it could continue to get worse. I can't imagine how I can manage on a lower dose with things the way they are now. I need help managing the anxiety I have now."

Practitioner [reinforcing interest in preparing for a taper]: "You'd like to start with ways you can better manage the way you feel now. Something more than just white-knuckling it through, one moment at a time. And then do the taper gradually so you can build your confidence for managing the anxiety and panic."

SHARED FOCUSING

• • • • • •

What skills did the practitioner use to help focus the conversation with Leona?

_____

_____

_____

_____

How does the practitioner continue to engage and partner with Leona while focusing?

_____

_____

_____

_____

How does the practitioner offer information in an MI-consistent way?

_____

_____

_____

_____

FOCUSING WHEN THE FOCUS IS UNCLEAR

Sometimes, the change focus is unclear—either because the person feels overwhelmed and isn't sure what direction will be most helpful, or because the person has a sense of where they want to go but are unsure about how to get there. It may also occur when we, as practitioners, lack the confidence or knowledge to guide the conversation to support the person's progress toward their goals. In these situations, the change focus only emerges after the practitioner and person work together to figure out what might be creating difficulties in the person's life.

One particular risk in such conversations is increased *chat time* about irrelevant topics. Chat time decreases the effectiveness of conversations about change. The ability to guide off-topic comments back to the change focus is a significant strength in focusing sensitive topics. For example:

> **Person:** "I know I shouldn't hit my child, but you should have seen what she did yesterday!"
>
> **Practitioner:** "What did she do yesterday?" [Opening the door to losing focus]

> **Person:** "I know I shouldn't hit my child, but you should have seen what she did yesterday!"
>
> **Practitioner:** "You'd like to learn effective ways to respond when her behavior really surprises you. You want to stop hitting her." [Holding the focus with empathy and partnering. Opening the door to forward momentum]

The following is an example of focusing when the person is unclear where to begin. The practitioner has been working with a person who is experiencing bipolar symptoms. The practitioner begins with a summary of a conversation in which the person expresses some concern about loss of sleep. As they consider that focus together, it opens the door to exploration of other potential focuses (i.e., relationship with roommate, job, medication, etc.). They may use an *agenda map* (more about that later) to keep track of these focuses and others that may arise.

> **Practitioner:** "You've noticed that you are feeling more and more energized and excited about your blog. You've been staying up late doing research and buying merchandise to test it out for your readers. At the same time, you've noticed that other things are getting harder, like missing work, being able to pay the rent, and making things okay with your roommate—like keeping the apartment clean. You've also expressed some concern about not getting enough sleep. It's pretty common to see these things happening as the feelings of excitement and energy intensify. What are your thoughts about what we might do next to be helpful to you?"
>
> **Person:** "I have tried to think of how to do this and I haven't been able to figure it out. I guess if we could talk about a place to start?"
>
> **Practitioner:** "Well, if you like I can share with you some information about some things that have helped others in similar situations, and we can see what you think. I'd like to hear your thoughts about how these ideas might work for you."
>
> **Person:** "Sure, let's start there."
>
> **Practitioner:** "People with experiences like yours often tell me that when they establish regular sleep routines, they start to feel more able to manage these sorts of situations."
>
> **Person:** "So sleep routines will help me feel like I can cope with my job and everything?"
>
> **Practitioner:** "It might help. We see a real connection between sleep and mood. As people get more regular sleep, they have more energy for managing what's most important to them. And

they seem to be able to plan ahead to accomplish the things that are meaningful to them. What do you think about that?"

Person: "So we work on my sleep first and then the stuff with my job and my roommate?"

Practitioner: "We could. Or there might be another way to do it that's more appealing to you. There are some other things that people have found helpful as well, in addition to the sleep routines. I could tell you about those as well if you want."

Person: "Sure, I'd like to know."

In subsequent conversations, clarifying the focus by linking it to an earlier conversation might be a helpful way to follow up on progress toward the person's goals: "I know last time we talked about *x*. Should we explore that further today? Or perhaps there's something else on your mind that is more pressing?"

WHEN THE FOCUS IS UNCLEAR

· · · · · ·

Think about a recent change conversation you had with someone where the focus of change was unclear from the beginning.

What are you doing to partner with this person to uncover what is getting in the way of determining a determining a change focus?

_____

_____

_____

What skills did you use to sustain partnering as you negotiated the shared focus of change?

_____

_____

_____

How did you feel about the outcome of this recent conversation?

_____

_____

_____

Is there anything you might want to do differently in a similar situation?

_____

_____

_____

FOCUSING PROMPTS

• • • • • •

When there is a clear focus with a single topic:

"I hear that *x* is your top priority. How I can be helpful as we work together on this?"

When you negotiate an agenda based on a menu of options:

"There are a number of things that we typically discuss with people who are looking to increase their access to services; these include *x*, *y*, and *z*. I'm wondering which of these is something you would be interested in exploring. Or perhaps there's something else?"

When you negotiate multiple focuses by sharing the agenda with the person:

- "I'm sure you have some priorities today. Let's get to those first, and, before you go, I want to look at a couple of things together as well."

- "Today we have about *x* minutes; let's take the first part of our time to talk about your top priority, and before you go, I'd like to explore a couple of other things with you."

When you navigate mandated concerns:

"For us to work together, we'll need to explore some topics related to why you were asked to come here. We don't have to start there—I'm wondering what concerns or priorities are most important to you."

When you want to revisit the focus of an earlier conversation:

"Last time we met we talked about *x*. Should we explore that further today, or perhaps there's something else on your mind today that's more pressing?"

When you only have time for a short session:

"What I thought we could do today is quickly explore what, if any, changes you might like to make around accessing services. I'd like to hear what makes this important to you and what your goals are for it."

Developing an "Early Win" Focus

The willingness to consider making a change can be chilled by worries a person has about what they might lose. Fear about choosing a direction for change can keep people from moving ahead even when they want to try something new. A person might experience an inner voice that says, "Be careful, you might make a wrong decision!" The person might describe their fear as related to past experiences of feeling routinely undermined or embarrassed, or it can be related to an earlier situation in which the person felt helpless. This can become a *no-win* attitude that can sound something like:

- "It's hard for me to try new things, I don't like to feel uncomfortable or unsure about what's going to happen. What if I lose my security?"
- "I've been avoiding taking on real challenges, keeping to a steady routine. It's better that way."
- "I have a hard time getting started. I do stupid things like clean my desk, delete my emails, play a game instead of starting the change I want."
- "Honestly, I get paralyzed by thinking about what if someone doesn't like my performance or thinks I don't deserve the opportunity."
- "I waste a lot of time trying to do things perfectly."

While these concerns are perfectly valid and are not to be dismissed lightly, helping a person identify an *early win* focus can help them develop momentum and confidence for an initial change. An early win is a helpful small step in the right direction that the person feels ready, willing, and able to do. The essence of the early win focus is that it helps the person build their momentum for change when they are struggling to commit to a change they want to make. With an early win focus, we can evoke what the person has to gain from the change experience. For example:

Gail has attended four sessions to address her depression. Originally triggered by a medication change, Gail was on a waiting list for more than a month before getting to see the practitioner. While she has some interest and willingness to follow through with between-session assignments, her heart doesn't seem to be in it. The practitioner reframes Gail's ambivalence about these assignments to bring forward her expertise and avoid triggering negative self-evaluation.

Practitioner [engaging]: "So Gail, I'm interested in hearing about your experience of our work so far. How do you feel it's going?"

Gail [shrugs]: "It's okay, I guess. I mean it seems to be helping…"

Practitioner: "Sounds like we've made some progress and at the same time, you are hoping there's something more for you. If you were to imagine what you want your life to be like, what would that look like?"

Gail: "Um, I guess it would be nice to feel interested in something again."

Practitioner: "You've mentioned that before. And it sounds like the activities we've planned so far are not sparking your interest. Am I right about that?"

Gail: "Well, they've helped a bit. I get out of the house to go to the gym or take a walk. I'm just not that excited about that. It's still better than staying in bed or just watching TV. I guess."

Practitioner [focusing]: "So part of the issue is, going to the gym or walking helps with your health goals, and that's better than the way things were. But it sounds like there may be other things you find more interesting."

> **Gail** [long pause, considering]: "I've been wondering about volunteering or something, but I don't know…"
>
> **Practitioner:** "Tell me more about that, what do you like about that idea?"

As they talk, Gail identifies an unmet desire to connect with others in meaningful ways. Gail is uncertain about how to initiate this and has avoided exploring this focus because she feared she would be disappointed and it would trigger even worse self-evaluation and depressed mood. As Gail explored her interest, the practitioner listened, bringing forward Gail's thoughts. Here, the practitioner summarizes what Gail has explored so far:

> **Practitioner** [summarizing Gail's ideas about potential focuses]: "So it sounds like you'd like to figure out a way to connect with others that feels safe to you. You've mentioned a couple of options you've considered: yoga classes, volunteer work, and joining something like a book club. At the same time that you want the connection, you talk yourself out of doing something because you don't want to be disappointed."
>
> **Gail:** "Yeah, I just can't get myself to go to yoga or a book club. I try, but I end up feeling too tired to go. I think I'm just way too self-conscious."
>
> **Practitioner:** "I wonder if I could offer some ideas that might help make it easier?"
>
> **Gail:** "Sure, go ahead."
>
> **Practitioner:** "Some people find it helpful to change the way they think about opportunities to connect with others to make it easier to move forward. Others find it easier to focus on doing something they love. Still others focus on breaking a change down into small manageable steps to take on one at a time. What do you think of these ideas? Or perhaps something else would work better for you?"
>
> **Gail:** "Um, so that reminds me, I got a call to play with this musician I've played with before. Maybe that would count? I was thinking of it as a way to make a little money."
>
> **Practitioner** [evoking]: "So it sounds like you are wondering if it could also be a way to make a connection. Tell me more about that. What do you think that would be like to play with them?"
>
> **Gail:** "I'm still self-conscious, but I'm confident about my music. It's easier to play than talk."

As Gail talks, her interest and confidence for playing music with others lifts and she moves quickly toward making a simple plan for accepting the job and explores how playing music might help her feel more connected to people.

TOOLS TO HELP IDENTIFY AND PRIORITIZE FOCUSES

Metaphor

Metaphors can help to make abstract concepts concrete. Martino and colleagues (2002) use the metaphor of a three-legged stool to explain the importance of the three goals for recovery from co-occurring disorders: being abstinent, taking medications, and engaging in treatment for co-occurring disorders. Using an actual small three-legged stool, they demonstrate the impact of removing one of the goals by removing one of the legs and letting the stool fall over. This demonstration is both entertaining and helps people understand how the three goals work together to support their progress toward their life goals.

Drawing Conversations About Change

Drawing conversations about change as they unfold helps people track conversations and improves organization and recall. When the person is willing to make the drawing themselves, offering options for pen colors and other materials can increase their engagement and exploration. Pointing to the relevant areas of the drawing while offering summaries helps to ground the conversation in the larger context and supports the transition from one focus to another and the transition to evoking. Images, words, and arrows help to highlight how different focus areas are related. The person can continue the drawing in evoking and planning and then take a copy of the drawing with them to remember their goals and next steps. The drawing can also be used to review their progress in the next session.

Agenda Mapping

Practitioners use *agenda mapping* to invite people to identify a good starting place for their work together. An agenda map can start out as a blank sheet of paper where the person or the practitioner writes down the person's potential change targets as they emerge during the conversation. It can also be a sheet of paper with empty circles (e.g., a *bubble sheet*) to be filled in by the person or the practitioner with possible change targets as they emerge during the conversation.

Agenda mapping is useful when a person's central goal involves change focuses that fall under one larger umbrella. For example, someone who wants to go back to school may have several change focuses related to that one goal (e.g., reducing debt, managing time, deciding whether to pursue online or live coursework). Similarly, someone who is interested in improving their overall health may want to address multiple concerns in different directions (e.g., increasing physical activity, reducing stress, balancing work and life, making different food choices, improving sleep hygiene). An agenda map in this circumstance can be a sheet of paper with some blank circles and some circles filled in in advance with change options that typically need to be considered when working toward the person's goal.

We can also use agenda mapping when we have change topics that *we* need to address with the person. We can start with the focuses that are most important to the person and then transition transparently to the focuses we need to address. Agenda mapping is a popular tool for practitioners who are short on time. It is also popular with practitioners who are early in their career and learning to navigate an array of change options while supporting autonomy. Here are some prompts that can help us get started cocreating an agenda map:

- "We will need to eventually create a plan together around substance use as a condition of your continuing to receive services here, so let's keep that topic on the table. You probably have some other things you'd like to work on together, and there's plenty of space here for you to include those ideas. We can start with one of those, if you like."
- "I know you have a number of concerns on your mind today as we get started working together. Here's some space for you to fill in those things so we can find a starting place for our discussion."
- "If you were to say, 'My life would be great right now except for *x*,' how would you fill in that blank? Let's focus on the topics that are in your control and put them on this agenda map."

Practitioners can also create *nested agenda maps*, in which the first agenda map contains the highest level of options (again, with several circles left blank for the person's own ideas). For example, if the person's goal is to manage their depressive symptoms, then the top sheet of the agenda map might have a range of high-level strategies, such as taking medications, neutralizing negative thoughts, and increasing pleasant daily activities. The subsequent sheet of the agenda map would contain the available options that fall under one of these more general areas. For example, under the strategy of "increasing pleasant daily activities," the person might include more specific focuses to help them achieve this goal, such as participating in community or playful activities, meditating, going out with friends, changing their environment, and engaging in spiritual or relaxation practices. Figure 4 is an example of a nested agenda map regarding health improvement; Figure 5 is an example of a follow-up agenda map focused on sleep.

Possible introduction:

"You mentioned that you are interested in improving your health. There are many different areas people choose to focus on. Here are some common ones. What looks most important for us to explore together? Or perhaps there's something else you wanted to talk about?"

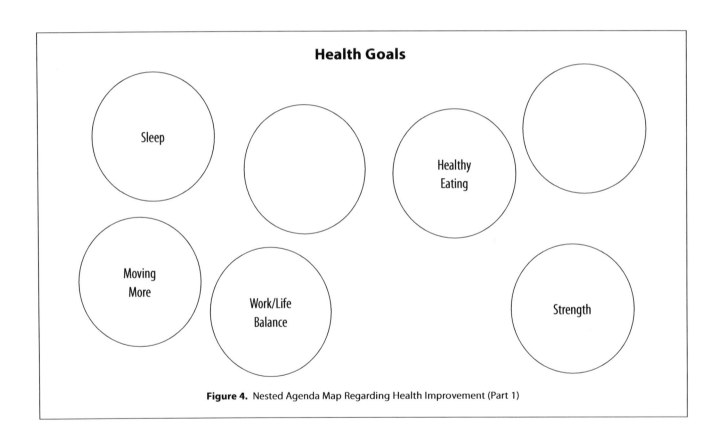

Figure 4. Nested Agenda Map Regarding Health Improvement (Part 1)

Possible introduction:

"You mentioned that you would like to start by improving your sleep. This is a topic that interests a lot of people and includes working on making it easier to fall asleep, sleep more, and wake up feeling refreshed. What are your thoughts about where you might like to start?"

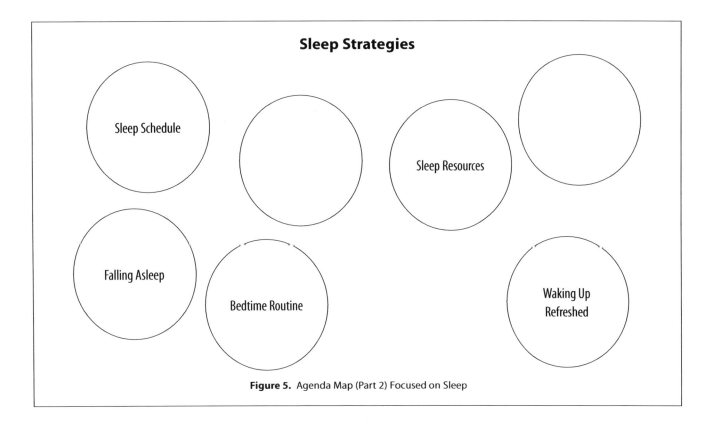

Figure 5. Agenda Map (Part 2) Focused on Sleep

Another way to use agenda maps is to encourage people to identify what they see as the most important areas of discussion, perhaps even before they meet with the practitioner. This has the advantage of inviting the person to consider their priorities while they are waiting for their appointment, and it places their concerns at the center of the conversation. People sometimes draw larger circles for their higher-priority focuses and smaller circles for their lower-priority focuses to highlight the focuses that are most important to them. Their personal agenda map can be included in their chart as a way to track their progress. They can cross out change focuses as they achieve their goals in those areas. In this manner, the agenda map becomes a concrete visual reminder of the gains that people have made.

This video provides a demonstration of the agenda mapping process:

- Motivational Interviewing in a Vocational Rehabilitation Setting: Using Agenda Mapping to Focus the Conversation: tinyurl.com/3hg63vq2

On the following pages you will find three samples of agenda maps depicting some topic areas related to anxiety, depression, and thought disorders, and a blank bubble sheet to use with the people with whom you work.

SAMPLE AGENDA MAP 1

• • • • • • •

"Here are some topics we can explore to support your goal to feel happier and more confident managing your mood. You may have other things you'd like to add. Then, we can find a good starting place."

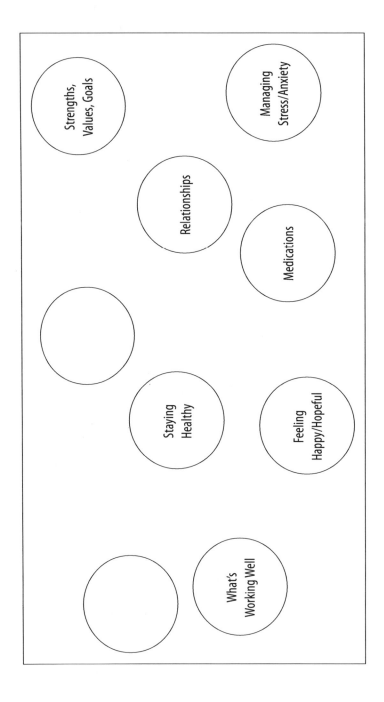

SAMPLE AGENDA MAP 2

• • • • • • •

"Here is a space for us to identify some topics we can explore to support your goal to feel more confident managing anxious feelings. I might make a couple of suggestions, and you may have other things you'd like to add. Then, we can find a good starting place."

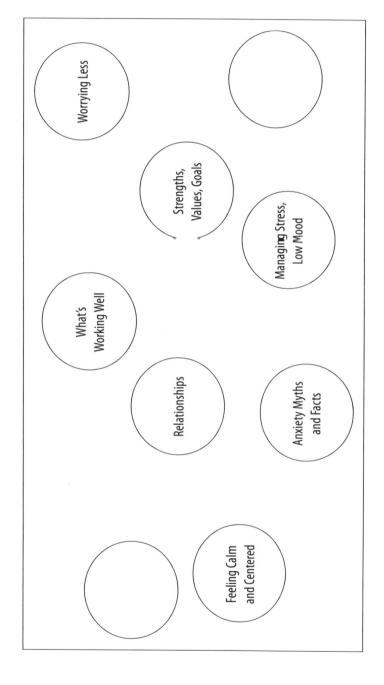

SAMPLE AGENDA MAP 3

• • • • • • •

"Here are some topics you've mentioned about areas of your life you'd like to work on together. You may have other things you'd like to add. Then, we can find a good starting place."

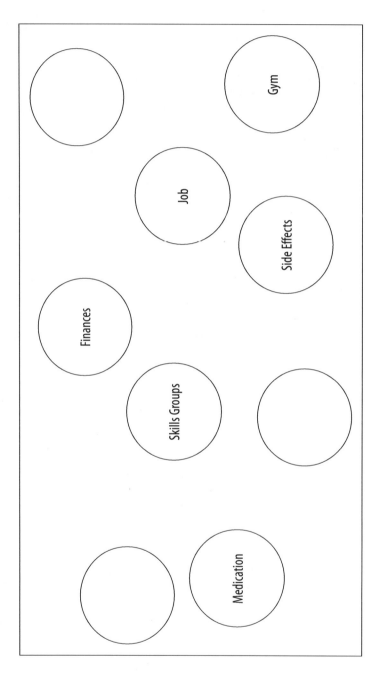

AGENDA MAP TEMPLATE

· · · · · · ·

THE DANCE OF MI: MOVING FROM FOCUSING TO EVOKING

The process of focusing is so important in conversations about change because arriving at an acceptable change focus *together* opens the door to evoking. In evoking, our attention turns toward the horizon. We hold the change focus steady and work together with the person to resolve their ambivalence and develop momentum for making the change. Our intention is to support the person in resolving their ambivalence about the change focus and begin to develop readiness for planning to support the change. It is important to know when to move from focusing to evoking and when to stay in or increase the focusing process.

Signals to Increase Focusing

- The person is covering too many topics and not orienting in a specific direction toward a specific change focus.
- The person seems overwhelmed and discouraged about making a change.

Practitioner Strategies to Increase Focusing

Try these strategies to sustain engagement and align or realign the focus of the conversation.

Seek Collaboration: Summarize the change topics that have emerged so far and ask about the person's highest priority change focus:

- "What's most important to you here?"

If there is a difficult change topic, ask permission to discuss it or include it in a range of options for the person to choose from:

- "I know you didn't plan to come here to talk about feeling sad, is it all right with you if we take a few moments to understand how that relates to these other issues?"

Emphasize Autonomy: Emphasize the person's right to choose their own focus of change.

- When conducting an assessment, offer a choice around the discussion of the person's priorities for change either before or after the assessment.
- Normalize the person's experience of the change process as difficult.
- Affirm the person's values, strengths, and aspirations for change based on what they've already said.
- Offer information and advice about potential focuses given a person's goals in an MI-consistent style.
- Avoid using persuasion, confrontation, too many questions, offering unsolicited advice, information, suggestions.

Signals to Guide Toward Evoking

The person has identified the direction in which they want to move and is ready to explore a change focus or focuses.

Practitioner Strategies to Guide Toward Evoking

- Check accurate understanding of the person's perspective, dilemma, and goals by summarizing what the person wants to focus on, any high-priority focuses to be addressed, and any additional focuses you might discuss.
- Reflect how the change focus relates to the person's values and goals.
- Reflect concerns that need to be addressed and any emerging change talk.
- Assess and explore the importance and confidence for making the change.
- Avoid arguing for change and telling the person how to change.

CHAPTER SUMMARY

• • • • • •

What do you see as the most important points of this chapter?

_____

_____

_____

_____

_____

What interested you the most?

_____

_____

_____

_____

_____

What focusing strategies are you most likely to try?

_____

_____

_____

_____

_____

7

EVOKING: PREPARATION FOR CHANGE

You cannot teach a man anything; you can only help him find it within himself.

—Galileo Galilei

IN THIS CHAPTER

- Language About Change

- Types of Change Talk

- Evoking and Responding to Change Talk

- Strengthening Acceptance and Developing Discrepancy

- Evoking Importance and Confidence

- Softening/Decreasing Sustain Talk

- Equipoise: Evoking Change Talk with Neutrality

- Tools to Aid Evoking

- A Bridge for Change

- The Dance of MI: From Evoking to Planning

The more someone talks about an attitude or belief, the more likely they are to believe it (Bem, 1972). In MI, we help a person move in the direction of change by paying careful attention to *how* they talk about the change under consideration and responding *differentially* to what they say about *making a change* and their *ambivalence about* the change. In this chapter we will explore helping people resolve their ambivalence in the direction of the change they want to make. We also explore a specialized approach called *developing discrepancy* to support people who are not thinking about making a change. Finally, we will look at how we intentionally maintain a neutral stance when supporting a person who is struggling with ambivalence about a difficult decision (e.g., whether to get a divorce, donate a kidney, adopt a child).

LANGUAGE ABOUT CHANGE

A first step in strengthening our ability to guide a person's exploration of the change they are considering is to recognize the different kinds of language people use when they talk about change:

- Change talk: Making statements that speak to DARN: desire ("I want to change"), ability ("I can change"), reasons ("I have several reasons to change"), or need ("I should change").

- Commitment language (CATS): commitment ("I will make the change"), activation ("I am ready to make the change"), taking steps ("I've already started taking steps to make the change").

- Discord: arguing, interrupting, or ignoring the practitioner—often in response to something the practitioner is doing to disrupt harmony or engagement ("You can't make me change," "You are wrong").

- Sustain talk: making statements that defend the status quo ("Things are fine as they are," "Change is too hard").

IDENTIFYING THE FOUR LANGUAGE TYPES

• • • • • •

Identify whether you think each statement reflects discord (D), sustain talk (S), change talk (CT), or commitment language (CL). If you think a statement contains more than one type, note that as well.

_____ 1. I'm not taking medications, and nothing you can say will make me!

_____ 2. The prescriptions are just too expensive. Mindfulness activities are all I can afford.

_____ 3. I know it's bad for me, but it really lifts my mood.

_____ 4. My mood is better when I eat well and get some exercise.

_____ 5. I'm going to clean out the pantry; no more sweet snacks for me. Sugar lifts me up and then my mood crashes.

_____ 6. I want to feel good when I go out to appointments, I'm tired of this anxiety.

_____ 7. You're not serious about this antidepression diet, are you?

_____ 8. Maybe I could try to eat breakfast some mornings; maybe that would help my mood.

_____ 9. I know what's good for my baby; I've had my struggles, but I'm doing better now.

_____ 10. A little extra sugar is good for my baby. I always feel better with some sugar, too.

_____ 11. My partner likes me like this, and I don't see anything wrong with that.

_____ 12. I already tried the meditation exercises since we last talked.

_____ 13. You and my doctor make way too much of this. I feel fine.

_____ 14. I will make sure to drink a glass of water with my medications; I know it's recommended.

_____ 15. If the pain gets worse, I'll have surgery. No more opiates for me.

TYPES OF CHANGE TALK

We refer to change talk and commitment language as two different types of change talk: Preparatory change talk and mobilizing change talk. *Preparatory* change talk is characterized by DARN for change. It comes first in the exploration of change as the person considers the possibility of making a change. *Mobilizing* change talk is characterized by CATS, and signals an increasing readiness for change and resolution of the person's ambivalence.

To support the person in developing momentum toward change, we support their exploration of DARN CATS. The more someone offers preparatory change talk, the more likely they are to offer mobilizing change talk. *The likelihood of change increases as a person's mobilizing change talk increases.* To resolve ambivalence and increase readiness for change we:

- Recognize change talk when it occurs.
- Respond to change talk by reinforcing it.
- Evoke or draw out change talk.
- Soften sustain talk.

We help the person explore how important the change is by responding *selectively* to what they say about their desire, reasons, and need for the change. We help the person explore how confident they are about making the change by responding selectively to what they say about their ability to make the change. The more the person talks about the importance and their confidence for the change, the more likely they are to explore how they could be successful. We call this envisioning. This shift toward envisioning signals to us to begin guiding the conversation toward the planning process and increasing *readiness* for change.

RECOGNIZING CHANGE TALK

• • • • • •

Before we can build change talk in our conversations, we need to recognize it when it occurs. Let's look at where you are right now. Think about a recent conversation you had with a person with whom you are working and answer the following questions about what you already know about their interest in making a change.

What has this person already told you about their perspective and priorities for making the change?

_____

_____

_____

_____

_____

How are you maintaining a steady and clear focus on the change throughout the conversation?

_____

_____

_____

_____

_____

What are you doing to evoke change talk?

_____

_____

_____

_____

_____

What does change talk sound like in your conversation about change?

_____

_____

_____

_____

When you hear change talk, what are you already doing to build on it?

_____

_____

_____

_____

How are you ensuring that certain activities (e.g., information gathering, providing information) do not interfere with your ability to evoke the person's change talk?

_____

_____

_____

_____

EVOKING AND RESPONDING TO CHANGE TALK

How we respond to change talk and sustain talk influences *how much* change talk emerges in the conversation. Like sunlight on a plant, plentiful attention to change talk increases the likelihood of change. Too much attention to sustain talk decreases the likelihood of change. The strategies that we use to respond to and evoke change talk fall under the acronym of *EARS*:

- **E**laborating and evocative questions: When a change talk theme emerges, ask for specific examples (e.g., "Tell me more." "What else?" "When was the last time that happened?"). To evoke change talk, ask for it (e.g., "Why would you want to make this change?" "If you decided to make this change, how would you go about it?").
- **A**ffirmations (e.g., "You're determined to persist with this until you make it").
- **R**eflections (e.g., "You've decided to make modeling healthy behavior for your kids a priority").
- **S**ummaries (e.g., "It hasn't been easy to figure out how you might succeed in making this change. You've really stuck with it, and you can now see some options for being successful. It's important to you to do this for your family, and you are determined to succeed").

With EARS in mind, let's check back in with Leona.

Practitioner: "What would you like to get out of our work together? What would you consider to be a good result?"

Leona: "If it works? Well, I guess it would be working if it actually helps me control my anxiety and panic attacks and helps me sleep better."

Practitioner: "Better control of the anxiety and panic attacks, and better sleep. What else?"

Leona: "If I'm not so irritable with my kids and at work. If I'm on time to work again."

Practitioner: "So it would make a difference in the morning with your kids and at work."

Leona: "Well that would be ... I really need some way to make mornings smoother. And work, too."

Practitioner: "So you are doing your best to take good care of your kids, do your work, and manage your anxiety. What are you doing already that helps you to manage the anxiety?"

Leona: "I guess I keep telling myself the feelings are going to end and to hold on until my next dose. I'm gritting my teeth and hanging on, waiting for it to end. It's really hard to believe it will get better."

Practitioner: "You know you are capable of hanging on until your next dose. That's some strong determination and self-control. It's not easy, but you've been doing it. What do you already know about yourself that has helped in other difficult situations?"

Leona: "Well, I made it through childbirth twice and my dad's death. Those were really overwhelming. I guess knowing what to expect, having my mom to talk to about it, and knowing my kids are counting on me."

Practitioner: "That's a lot to manage. You made it through painful and overwhelming things and knowing what to expect, thinking about your kids, and having someone to talk to helped. How might that help you now?"

Leona: "Well, I guess knowing that the medication is actually making the anxiety worse. I guess I need to find some ways to cope on less medication…maybe then I can get off it and it will get better."

Practitioner: "And let's say that happens, you get off of the medication, you have effective ways to manage the anxiety, your sleep improves, what might your life be like in, say, a year?"

Leona: "Well [laughs], still chaotic. My kids are still going to be a lot to handle. But that's okay, they're worth it. I guess I'll be happier, calmer, work will be better. Maybe I'll have some energy to make some new friends."

Practitioner: "So let's take a look at where we are and where we are going. Your physician is concerned about your recent request to increase your medication dose. You are concerned about the long-term effects of staying on the medication. You've been managing to tolerate the anxiety so far by gritting your teeth and telling yourself to hold on until your next dose. You know you can tolerate painful and overwhelming experiences and it's easier if you know what to expect and have someone to talk to. You are hoping to eventually taper off of this medication and have a smoother morning routine, better sleep, and better control over the anxiety. What would you like to do?"

Leona: "Well, I don't know. I guess I need a better way to manage the anxiety, panic attacks, and irritability I have now."

Practitioner: "You'd like to find some strategies for managing the panic attacks you are having now and then gradually taper off of the medication."

Leona: "Yes, that's what I'd like to do."

EARS

• • • • • •

Part 1

Mark up the conversation with Leona with an *E*, *A*, *R*, or *S* per these questions:

- What elaborating and evocative questions does the practitioner use? (E)
- What affirmations do you see? (A)
- What reflections does the practitioner offer? (R)
- What summaries do you see? (S)

Part 2

What are some examples of sustain talk from Leona?

_____

_____

_____

_____

Examples of change talk?

_____

_____

_____

_____

What does Leona say that signals some resolution of her ambivalence about whether and why to make the change?

_____

_____

_____

_____

_____

ELICITING AND REINFORCING CHANGE TALK

• • • • • •

Consider the pieces of conversation that follow and:

- Write a practitioner comment or question that might have elicited the person's statement.

- Write something that you might say to positively reinforce the person's statement, perhaps using an affirmation or a reflection.

Note: Refrain from giving advice or offering suggestions; instead, your answers should simply express support or show understanding.

Example

Practitioner [elicit]: "What are some things that increase your feelings of well-being?"

Person: "I feel better when I sleep well."

Practitioner [reinforce]: "Good sleep is important to you and your sense of wellness. You already know some ways to get good sleep, and you feel better when you do."

Practitioner [elicit]:

_____

_____

_____

_____

_____

Person: "I want to feel good when I go out to appointments. I'm tired of this anxiety."

Practitioner [reinforce]:

_____

_____

_____

_____

Practitioner [elicit]:

_____

_____

_____

_____

Person: "Maybe I could try to eat breakfast some mornings; that would help my mood."

Practitioner [reinforce]:

_____

_____

_____

_____

Practitioner [elicit]:

_____

_____

_____

_____

Person: "I think I can walk twice a week with my neighbor; it helps the depression I've been feeling, and she's a good support for me."

Practitioner [reinforce]:

_____

_____

_____

_____

Practitioner [elicit]:

_____

_____

_____

_____

Person: "I know I should take this stuff seriously; I just don't want to."

Practitioner [reinforce]:

_____

_____

_____

_____

Now try some statements that you are likely to hear in your own practice using the same pattern:

You [elicit]:

_____

_____

_____

_____

_____

Person:

_____

_____

_____

_____

You [reinforce]**:**

_____

_____

_____

_____

You [elicit]**:**

_____

_____

_____

_____

Person:

_____

_____

_____

_____

You [reinforce]:

_____

_____

_____

_____

You [elicit]:

_____

_____

_____

_____

Person:

_____

_____

_____

_____

You [reinforce]:

_____

_____

_____

_____

STRENGTHENING ACCEPTANCE AND DEVELOPING DISCREPANCY

People sometimes express no interest in change or appreciation for the impact their choices have on their functioning. Take, for example, a person who holds strongly to a belief that is a barrier to improving their functioning and achieving their goals. Perhaps this is someone who is willing to return to homelessness because they have a fixed belief that the housing program staff are stealing from them. Or perhaps this is someone who feels intense anxiety and believes it is protecting them from harm. If we try to argue with the person's belief, we run the risk of creating discord. On the other hand, if we build an accepting foundation that places a priority on understanding the person's perspective, respecting their autonomy, communicating their absolute worth, and affirming their strengths, skills, intentions, and efforts, then they might be more willing to explore other perspectives. This gentle approach to increasing safety, understanding, and acceptance of the person's sustain talk before exploring the change side of the person's ambivalence is called *developing discrepancy*. An example of gently asking permission to have a conversation about change following such a foundation might start by wondering about the possibility of looking at the person's belief and offering autonomy to postpone the conversation for another time. For example:

> **Practitioner:** "It sounds like we may see things differently here. It might be helpful sometimes to think about how we've come to our different conclusions. If you aren't ready to have that conversation, you can just say so. It's your choice. How does that sound to you?"
>
> **Person:** "Not today. Maybe later."

This respectful, autonomy-supportive approach helps maintain and strengthen our MI-consistent practice when we are tempted to argue for change and to offer information without permission.

Developing discrepancy is not intended to be a way to make people see the consequences of their behavior and choices. It is a way to work together with a person; to understand and accept their experience, interests, and concerns; and to increase the person's sense of safety and willingness to explore the other side of their ambivalence.

Exploring strong ambivalence about beliefs or behaviors means responding to moment-to-moment shifts in the person's motivation. If the change side of the person's ambivalence is strongest, then we explore that. If the person changes the subject or brings forward the sustain side of their ambivalence, we understand and explore that. If dissonance emerges, we respond with empathy and deep acceptance. Strengthening trust and safety in the relationship increases the person's openness to exploring their motivation and options for change. Someone who has struggled with an issue for a long time may benefit from multiple sessions to explore and resolve their ambivalence about making a change. As the person explores their ambivalence for making a change, we guide toward evoking information about reasons for change from their experience and goals.

In the following conversation, the practitioner explores how the person's goals are related to their ambivalence about taking medication. One side of this ambivalence might be "Having to stay on medication undermines my autonomy and independence" and the other side might be "I have been able to spend more time with my loved ones and can work when I stay on medication." As the practitioner demonstrates understanding and acceptance about the person's dilemma, the person becomes more forthcoming about their own insights into how the medication supports their success:

> **Person:** "I don't like feeling fat and tired. That's the medication."
>
> **Practitioner:** "That's something you'd like to change."

Person: "Yeah, when I live by myself, I won't take the medication anymore."

Practitioner: "When you don't need to rely on the program anymore for a place to live."

Person: "Yeah, I'll have my own place."

Practitioner: "You see stopping your medication and having your own place as things you can do when you are independent and making your own decisions."

Person: "I lost my place when I thought I was cured."

Practitioner: "You got your own place and felt so well you stopped taking your medication."

Person: "Yeah, I thought I didn't need it."

Practitioner: "And now you want to have your own place without feeling fat and tired."

Person: "Yeah. I don't want to relapse again."

Practitioner: "You see how medications help you feel well and keep your own place. It sounds like you might want some ideas about feeling well and energetic while staying on medications. So you can be independent and not relapse."

This example demonstrates how frequent complex reflections can gently communicate acceptance that behaviors and beliefs are understandable, adaptive, and even necessary based on the person's experience. This helps shift the conversation to a larger, more strengths-based context, increasing self-compassion, deepening exploration, and creating opportunities to explore changes they can make if they choose to.

EVOKING IMPORTANCE AND CONFIDENCE

To increase readiness for change, we seek to support the person's exploration of the *importance* of the change and *confidence* in their ability to make the change. To do so, we pay close attention to the strength of the person's change talk, so we know where to guide the person's exploration of the change under consideration. For example, if a person is making ambivalent statements about importance and confidence, reflections can increase the person's exploration of these areas:

Person: "I want to lose weight, but my knees hurt too much to do the walking I'm supposed to do."

Practitioner [guiding toward increasing confidence]: "You see the benefits of losing weight, and you are looking for daily exercises you can do without so much pain."

Person: "I'm supposed to eat less sugar. I'm just not sure it's worth it."

Practitioner [guiding toward increasing importance]: "You're not sure eating less sugar is worth the effort, and you may be interested in hearing more about the benefits for your mood."

Person: "I need to take my medication daily, but it's hard to remember."

Practitioner [guiding toward increasing commitment]: "You're looking for a foolproof way to remember to take your medications daily."

Evocative questions support exploration of change talk and focus on the person's perceived importance of and confidence in making the change. Remembering to use reflections, affirmations, and summaries in addition to evocative questions helps us ensure that we are maintaining partnership and empathy while evoking. Using many accurate complex reflections helps with guiding the conversation forward and increasing its depth and momentum. You might consider developing a habit of always reflecting change talk when you hear it. This practice will help to develop your ability to hear implied change talk when it is offered and guide the conversation using reflections and summaries.

Evoking Importance

People won't make a change unless they believe that change is important. We can explore a person's own desire, reasons, and need for change (i.e., importance change talk) using:

- Evocative and elaborating questions about the importance of the change.
- Affirmations about the person's values and intentions for change.
- Reflections and summaries to:
    - Reinforce and deepen the person's exploration of the importance of the change.
    - Reflect implied importance change talk.
    - Reframe qualities that might seem positive about the behavior (e.g., high tolerance for alcohol, worrying helps to keep family safe) to highlight the inherent risks of the behavior (e.g., harmful to liver, detracts from enjoying time with family).

As people explore whether and why to make a change, they offer information about how important the change is to them. It is helpful to evoke why they *want* to make the change and/or why they feel they *need* to make the change and then reflect what they say about the importance of change.

Ask Evocative and Elaborating Questions to Evoke Importance

Evocative questions can be used to initiate exploration of the importance of change. Elaborating questions (e.g., "Tell me more," "What else?") are easy ways to build change talk once it starts. Reflections, affirmations, and summaries deepen and guide the person's exploration. Evocative questions about importance may sound like:

- "What is it about this change that is important to you?"
- "What are your three best reasons for making this change?"
- "Why do you feel that it is important to make this change now?"

Ask Hypothetical Questions to Evoke Importance

Hypothetical questions are helpful ways to evoke initial change talk when it is not otherwise forthcoming. They guide the person in remembering a time (looking back) when things were better. Or looking forward, to imagine how things might be if the person makes the change compared to how they will be if the person doesn't make the change. These explorations are starting places for early change talk. The practitioner's skill is in guiding the exploration of change (i.e., whether and why) to develop momentum for envisioning how and when the person might make the change.

- **Look back:** Ask about a time before the current concern emerged: "How were things better? Different?"

- **Look forward:** Ask what may happen if things continue as they are:
  - "If you do make these changes, what will your life be like, say six months from now (or whatever time frame makes sense)?" "And if you don't make these changes?"
  - "If you were 100 percent successful in making the changes you want, what would be different?"
  - "What would have to happen for you to decide to make this change?"
  - "How would you know when it is time for you to make a change?"
- **Ask about extremes:** Ask the person to imagine the worst possible outcome of maintaining the status quo versus the best possible outcome of change. Maintaining a strong rapport is important. These questions are designed to help the person explore a change they are considering for themselves. Discord can arise when the person feels these questions are about the practitioner's agenda.
  - "What are the worst things that might happen if you don't make this change?"
  - "What are the best things that might happen if you do make this change?"
- **Use reflections and summaries** to deepen the person's exploration of these themes and affirmations to highlight the person's values and intentions for change.

Highlight Goals and Values to Evoke Importance

A person's goals and values are part of their intrinsic motivation for change. Values exploration can be used during evoking to bring forward change talk and increase momentum for change. Exploring or reexploring goals and values helps to evoke the importance of change. Returning to the values grid or card sort exercise (Chapter 5) you might review what the person's guiding values are and how they are related to the change under consideration:

- "What do you want in life? What is most important to you?"
- "How does moving in the direction of the change fit with your goals or values?"
- "How does making the change help you live your important values more fully?"

Using a change ruler or change thermometer (see "Tools to Aid in Evoking," which follows) can also be helpful for evoking importance.

Evoking Confidence

People won't make a change unless they are confident that they can do it. Sometimes, importance is low because confidence is low, and it's not until the person sees their own ability to make a change that they begin to more seriously consider making it. We can develop confidence change talk using:

- Evocative and elaborating questions to elicit information about the person's strengths, skills, intentions, wisdom, and abilities.
- Affirmations to highlight the person's unique strengths, skills, efforts, and abilities.
- Reflections and summaries to:
  - Reinforce, deepen, and guide the person's exploration of their ability to make the change.

- Reflect implied change talk—both preparatory and mobilizing—to guide toward developing momentum for change.
- Reframe qualities that might seem negative to the person (e.g., stubbornness) to underscore the person's inherent strengths (e.g., persistence, resilience).

Reflections that reframe a perceived "failure" as evidence of persistence are especially helpful when confidence is low. Failure has a deficit component to it. In contrast, effort, persistence, and "trying" are strengths-based characteristics that bring forward the person's persistence and increase the likelihood of their success. Reframing a perceived deficit as a strength can have an affirming quality that increases confidence. For example:

Person: "I've tried to do the assignment, I've tried first thing in the morning, before bed, and during lunch; I can't seem to focus on it."

Practitioner: "You've been really persistent with this and may be looking for some ways to make it easier to focus."

Person: "Well, I'm worried about the other applicants. I'm probably older than they are."

Practitioner: "You are wondering if your age will limit your options and at the same time it might give you an advantage because you have more experience than the younger applicants."

Person: "I've tried walking and I've tried water aerobics and I haven't been able to stick to it."

Practitioner: "You've really put some effort into this and learned a lot about what it will take to make it work for you. You're looking for ways to make it an easier part of your routine."

Ask Questions That Evoke Confidence

Evocative and elaborating questions bring forward the person's ideas, strengths, skills, intentions, and efforts for making the change. Elaborating questions (e.g., "Tell me more," "What else?") are easy ways to build confidence change talk once it starts. Evocative questions initiate exploration of the person's confidence for change:

- "If you were to decide to make this change, how might you do it?"
- "You know yourself best, what do you think will help you be successful?"
- "What do you already know about yourself that makes you think you could do this?"

When confidence is low for a particular change focus, we can broaden the conversation to talk about other times the person has made a successful change. Evocative questions bring forward the person's strengths, skills, and efforts in earlier changes. Elaborating questions (e.g., "Tell me more," "What else?") build the person's story about a past successful change and identify ideas for success with the current change. Reflections and summaries deepen and guide the person's exploration of their efforts in successful changes and activate the person's own ideas for the change under consideration. Affirmations highlight the person's strengths, skills, and abilities that might be helpful with the current change. Qualities that seem negative to the person can be reframed and affirmed to highlight the person's inherent strengths.

- "What changes have you made in your life that were difficult for you?"
- "How did you do that?"
- "Why did you decide to make that change?"
- "To what do you attribute your success?"

Ask Hypothetical Questions That Evoke Confidence

When confidence is low, it sometimes helps to explore the change in hypothetical terms. This relieves the pressure of needing a plan. It frees the person up to imagine a different future without having to start working on that future now. The idea is to help the person imagine future success with a quality of "when you are ready."

- "If you did decide to make this change at some point in the future, how might you do it?"
- "If you were going to brainstorm with a friend about how they might make this change, what ideas would you offer?"
- "What might it take to make this change?"
- "If you imagine things were different and this barrier wasn't in your way, how would you make this change?"
- "Suppose you did succeed with this change and that you were looking back on it now. What most likely worked? How did it happen?"

Envisioning Success

Evoking confidence for change increases opportunities to explore the person's strengths, abilities, and resources. In addition to reflecting change talk whenever you hear it, you may want to be particularly attuned to *implied envisioning* for making a change. Envisioning what a person's life might be like if they are successful in making a change supports intrinsic motivation for making that change. We can guide these conversations by exploring the benefits of pursuing a person's goals, prioritizing initial steps (e.g., coping skills and specific activities), and evoking change talk about the person's reasons for making the change:

- "What might your life be like if you made these activities a part of your week?"
- "How would that help you reach your goal?"
- "What benefits would you get from doing these activities?"

People who are further along in their readiness to make a change (i.e., offering mobilizing change talk) may express concerns about barriers that could interfere with how and when to make the change. This may sound like sustain talk but could actually be the person *envisioning* making the change (i.e., thinking about what making a change might look like for them). This is a signal to explore the person's ideas for addressing those barriers and possibly offering some ideas for their consideration. For example:

Person [envisioning]: "I'm going to stop, but I'm not ready to yet."

Practitioner [reflecting mobilizing change talk]: "You know you are going to stop."

Person: "Yes, I know."

Practitioner [evoking mobilizing change talk]: "How will you know when you are ready?"

Person: "When I know how I'll be able to decompress from work without drinking."

Practitioner: "So you'll know you are ready to make this change when you have a good idea what to do instead of drinking. That will help you prepare."

Person: "Right, I need some good ideas for leaving work at work and enjoying my free time."

Practitioner [evoking the person's ideas]: "And what ideas do you have for what might help?"

Person: "I used to work out. I could do that again, or I might try meditation."

Practitioner [evoking activation]: "You'd like to try working out again and maybe some meditation. What might you do to get started?"

Person: "I could get a membership at a gym again. Once I have that I know I'll go."

Practitioner: "So getting a membership seems like a first step to your goal."

Person: "Yeah, I used to really enjoy that. In fact, I probably shouldn't wait, or I may not do it. I'll just get that tomorrow."

Practitioner: "You sound really ready to get started."

Person: "Definitely. I know if I decide to go right after work, I'll do it. If I pack my gym clothes tonight, I'll take them with me and work out while I'm there."

Practitioner [evoking reasons to strengthen commitment]: "You've made up your mind. You want to start going to the gym tomorrow. Why would you do that?"

Person: "I need to stop drinking, and I already know I can. I think this will help me decompress and feel better about myself and my health."

Practitioner: "You have a lot of reasons to start working out: your health, your mood, how you feel about yourself. And you have a plan you can start right away."

Person: "Yes, I'm going to pack my bag tonight and start back at the gym tomorrow after work."

Recognizing envisioning makes it possible for the practitioner to guide a conversation that develops the person's intention to move toward making the change in a way that increases their confidence for success.

SOFTENING/DECREASING SUSTAIN TALK

Tension is often the life of a play. It is the twist that adds drama and excitement to the plot. Viewing sustain talk or discord as a perverse character flaw is a sad mistake, for these lie at the very heart of human change. They arise from the motives and struggles of the actors and foreshadow certain ends to which the play may or may not lead. The true art of a counselor is tested in recognizing and handling these tensions. It is on this stage that the drama of change unfolds.

—Bill Miller (Miller & Rollnick, 2013, p. 211)

Another strategy that supports people in developing momentum for change involves softening what the person says about keeping things the same (*sustain talk*). Examples of sustain talk include:

- "I don't want to make a change." [desire not to change]
- "I'm not able to make a change." [no ability to change]

- "I don't have good reasons to make a change." [reasons not to change]
- "I don't need to make a change." [no need to change]
- "I will not make a change." [commitment to not change]
- "I am not ready to make a change." [no activation to change]
- "I've already started taking steps so I do not have to make the change." [taking steps to not change]

Sustain talk offers important signals about the person's dilemma for making the change. We do what we can to avoid unnecessarily evoking and building sustain talk while honoring the person's experience and wisdom. The likelihood of change *increases* as sustain talk frequency *decreases* over the course of a conversation. Softening sustain talk involves:

- Recognizing sustain talk when it occurs.
- Responding effectively to sustain talk to soften the impact and reduce the frequency.
- Evoking or drawing out the other side of the person's ambivalence (i.e., change talk).
- Recognizing the difference between sustain talk and envisioning (e.g., "I'm not going to be successful making this change until I figure out how to avoid *x*").

Understanding the person's concerns can bring forth the change talk side of their ambivalence or at least their willingness to explore the potential for change.

Responding to Sustain Talk and Discord

When sustain talk is strong, we reflect the person's point of view in a way that respects it without reinforcing it. That is, *we dance with the sustain talk rather than building on it.* Strong sustain talk is common for people who experience intense anxiety or significant distress (e.g., related to histories of trauma, a lived experience of coercive treatment, or repeated experiences of trying and failing to make an important change). As with developing discrepancy, we start by establishing understanding and acceptance of the person's reluctance to make a change and guide toward increasing their willingness to explore the possibility of change. This respectful approach increases trust and safety and reduces the likelihood that we will encounter reactance or evoke discord. The following are examples of strong sustain talk.

Sustain talk about *importance* might sound like:

- "Is it really that important?"
- "I have other things that I need to do right now."
- "There really isn't a good reason for me to bother with this."

Sustain talk about *confidence* might sound like:

- "Does it have to be so complicated?"
- "I can't do this right now."
- "I tried before and failed. I just can't do it."

There are also times when the person is disinterested or disgruntled right from the start. How we deal with this discord and work to increase engagement is important. The more discord there is, the less likely we will be able to work together, and the less likely it is that the person will be able to focus on making a change. Fortunately, we receive fairly immediate feedback about the effectiveness of our approach. If discord decreases, our strategy is effective. If not, we need to shift strategies. This means returning to the engaging process to build or rebuild a *working alliance* before focusing the conversation and evoking change talk. Reflections are the preferred skill for working with people who present with a lot of sustain talk or discord.

There are a variety of strategies we can use to soften sustain talk and reduce discord. These include reflections (simple, complex, and double-sided), shifting focus, reframing, emphasizing autonomy, seeking collaboration, coming alongside, and agreement with a twist.

Simple reflections are a good general strategy for responding to sustain talk and discord. A simple acknowledgment of the person's disagreement, emotion, or perception can open the door to further exploration rather than defensiveness, arguments, and "Yes, but..." responses.

> **Person:** "It's not like I can just go out and get new friends!"
>
> **Practitioner:** "Making friends is not easy."

Complex reflections add or infer additional meaning and can be particularly effective when the added content is affirming.

> **Person:** "I'm trying! If you guys would just get off my back, I could focus on getting my life in order!
>
> **Practitioner:** "It's frustrating having someone looking over your shoulder" *or* "As time goes on, you're getting these things sorted out."

Double-sided reflections acknowledge the person's sustain talk as one side of their ambivalence while adding their change talk to the other side. Double-sided reflections sometimes include material that the person has previously offered, possibly in an earlier conversation.

> **Person:** "I don't smoke any more than most of my friends. What's wrong with having a joint now and then?"
>
> **Practitioner:** "This is confusing for you. It seems like you're not smoking any more than your friends, and at the same time—like you said last time we met—you don't like feeling so lazy after you've been smoking."

Shifting focus moves the focus of the conversation away from whatever barrier is standing in the way of exploring a change. This includes changing the topic or moving around roadblocks rather than trying to climb over them. Such detouring can soften sustain talk and defuse discord when exploring particularly difficult change topics.

> **Person:** "I feel like the counselor is out to get me or something!"
>
> **Practitioner:** "It's hard feeling like you're not sure you can trust them. It sounds like that may take some time."

Reframing acknowledges the validity of the person's perspective and offers a new meaning or interpretation. This is like recasting the person's perspective in a new light that supports exploration of change.

> **Person:** "I've tried so many times, and I haven't been able to do it."
>
> **Practitioner:** "You're very persistent, even when it hasn't worked out. This is really important to you."

Emphasizing personal choice and control early in conversations about change shows that we understand that the person is free to decide what they will ultimately do. This assurance reduces the likelihood that the person will feel they need to assert their independence (e.g., "I'll show you; nobody tells me what to do!"). Emphasizing autonomy is also helpful during conversations that often evoke sustain talk and discord such as offering information and advice.

> **Person:** "No one can tell me what to do!"
>
> **Practitioner:** "Yes, it's ultimately your decision how you handle this. Probation will expect certain things from you to maintain your freedom. But in the end, you are the only person who can decide what you'll do."

Seeking collaboration includes asking the person what they want to work on together, asking permission to share information, and asking for the person's thoughts about information or ideas for next steps. Seeking collaboration demonstrates respect and intent to work collaboratively with the person. Sometimes, the person's priorities differ from the practitioner's (and other's), and this can be a source of difficulty. When we partner with the person to explore a focus that is important to them, we create opportunities to also explore how the person's desired goals are related to the issues that we and others are concerned about.

> **Person:** "Every time I come in here, we talk about getting a job. You know I can't get a job until I have my license!"
>
> **Practitioner:** "It seems like working on the job is pretty difficult without the license, and I know it's important to you to get your license back. What would be most helpful for us to talk about today?"

Coming alongside is essentially siding with the person's sustain talk and even amplifying it a bit so the person is free to explore the change talk side of their ambivalence. This can be particularly helpful when the person seems stuck in the status quo. When using this approach, it is important to convey deep respect and appreciation for the person's perspective. It is helpful to practice coming alongside with colleagues to make sure that our tone conveys respect and appreciation before using this approach in a conversation about change.

> **Person:** "I know I'm never going to get a job. No one with a felony ever gets a decent job."
>
> **Practitioner:** "It's pretty much hopeless from your perspective. You can't imagine it ever happening, no matter what you do."

Agreement with a twist offers a reflection in which the practitioner reflects the person's sustain talk and then offers a slight reframe or change of direction. The momentum of the reflection carries the conversation in the direction of change.

> **Person:** "I don't mind going to counseling, but I don't want a counselor who isn't in recovery."
>
> **Practitioner:** "It's not the counseling itself you object to. You want a counselor who genuinely understands and respects your experience."

Responding Differentially to Develop Skillfulness

Our responses can "spin" or guide conversations about change in different directions. Perhaps counterintuitively, practicing evoking discord and sustain talk develops our skills for responding differentially to what a person says. As we strengthen our ability to recognize responses that may intensify discord and sustain talk, we are also strengthening our ability to guide in the direction of building momentum for change.

EVOKING DIFFERENTIALLY— PUT A SPIN ON IT

· · · · · ·

This exercise invites you to consider several statements and to create four different kinds of responses that evoke or emphasize discord, only sustain talk, only change talk, and both sustain talk and change talk.

Examples

Person: "I'm not sure how I can do all these things that the case manager is asking me to do."

Possible practitioner responses to evoke/emphasize:

Discord: "Well, you need to start because this is very serious!"

Sustain talk: "It looks discouraging to you."

Change talk: "You're looking for a way to make this work for you."

Both: "While it seems daunting, you're trying to find a way to get started."

Person: "When I eat better, I feel better."

Possible practitioner responses to evoke/emphasize:

Discord: "Given that, I'm surprised you don't make more of an effort."

Sustain talk: "It's hard to do all the time."

Change talk: "You're discovering a strong connection between how you eat and how you feel."

Both: "It can be difficult, and you really see a difference when you eat well."

Now try it for yourself.

Person: "Usually, I have a hangover on Monday morning before work, but not this week."

Your possible responses to evoke/emphasize:

Discord: _____

_____

Sustain talk: _____

_____

Change talk: _____

_____

Both: _____

_____

Person: "I remember to take my medication with meals about half the time."

Your possible responses to evoke/emphasize:

Discord: _____

_____

Sustain talk: _____

_____

Change talk: _____

_____

Both: _____

_____

Person: "I think my partner worries too much. I feel okay most of the time."

Your possible responses to evoke/emphasize:

Discord: _____

_____

Sustain talk: _____

_____

Change talk: _____

_____

Both: _____

_____

Person: "My doctor doesn't understand how hard it is for me to make so many changes."

Your possible responses to evoke/emphasize:

Discord: _____

_____

Sustain talk: _____

_____

Change talk: _____

_____

Both: _____

_____

Person: "I journaled about my mood and my thoughts every day this week."

Your possible responses to evoke/emphasize:

Discord: _____

_____

Sustain talk: _____

_____

Change talk: _____

_____

Both: _____

_____

Person: "Getting out to walk in the mornings has been very helpful for my mood."

Your possible responses to evoke/emphasize:

Discord: _____

_____

Sustain talk: _____

_____

Change talk: _____

_____

Both: _____

_____

Person: "I think I need to do something about my worrying, Sometimes I think it's helping but then I notice that it actually takes time away from enjoying my family."

Your possible responses to evoke/emphasize:

Discord: _____

_____

Sustain talk: _____

_____

Change talk: _____

_____

Both: _____

_____

Person: "I wish everyone would stop nagging me. I know what's best for me."

Your possible responses to evoke/emphasize:

Discord: _____

_____

Sustain talk: _____

_____

Change talk: _____

_____

Both: _____

_____

Person: "When I make my mind up, I can usually follow through on my good ideas."

Your possible responses to evoke/emphasize:

Discord: _____

_____

Sustain talk: _____

_____

Change talk: _____

_____

Both: _____

_____

Here are some opportunities for you to record and respond to statements that you often hear in your own practice.

The person says: _____

_____

Your possible responses to evoke/emphasize:

Discord: _____

_____

Sustain talk: _____

_____

Change talk: _____

_____

Both: _____

_____

The person says: _____

_____

Your possible responses to evoke/emphasize:

Discord: _____

_____

Sustain talk: _____

_____

Change talk: _____

_____

Both: _____

_____

The person says: _____

_____

Your possible responses to evoke/emphasize:

Discord: _____

_____

Sustain talk: _____

_____

Change talk: _____

_____

Both: _____

_____

The person says: _____

_____

Your possible responses to evoke/emphasize:

Discord: _____

_____

Sustain talk: _____

_____

Change talk: _____

_____

Both: _____

_____

EQUIPOISE: EVOKING CHANGE TALK WITH NEUTRALITY

There are times when we feel that it is important to maintain a neutral stance and support the person in reaching their own decision about a change. For example, a person may be deciding whether or not to take a promotion; to bear or adopt children; to start a modest, moderate, or intensive exercise program; to go back to school; to engage in treatment for an illness; or to donate an organ.

Equipoise can be described as "a conscious, intentional decision not to use one's own professional presence and skills to influence a [person] toward making a specific choice or change." (Miller & Rollnick, 2013, p. 233). Here, we transparently express our intention to remain neutral. We make particular efforts to help the person fully explore the pros and cons of the change under consideration so that they arrive freely at a decision for the direction they want to go.

When a person is exploring whether or not they want to make a change, we want to inform them that we are there to help them explore their dilemma and that we intend to remain neutral until they decide on their own direction. It is important that we normalize how difficult and uncomfortable this exploration can be, and that our intention is to help them work through this dilemma and support their autonomy in deciding for themselves.

When the person decides on a direction for change, we consider whether they still have unresolved ambivalence that interferes with their ability to make a plan for change. When needed, we shift out of equipoise and into the process of helping them resolve their ambivalence in their desired direction. "Tools to Aid Evoking" offers some ways to structure equipoise conversations and conversations that increase change talk and resolve ambivalence about change.

TOOLS TO AID EVOKING

The Change Ruler

Change rulers can help guide evocative conversations about importance, confidence, and commitment to change within the MI spirit. Here are some instructions and tools for guiding using change rulers. Remember to use reflections, affirmations, and summaries in addition to the evocative questions that follow.

USING CHANGE RULERS

· · · · · ·

To evoke importance:

Ask: "On a scale from 1 to 10, how important is it to you to change [insert focus behavior here], where 1 is not at all important and 10 is very important?"

Follow up: "And why are you at a _____ [whatever number they stated] and not a _____ [lower number than they stated]?"

Then: "What reasons or values do you have that might move you from a _____ to [higher number]?"

To evoke confidence:

Ask: "On a scale from 1 to 10, how confident are you that you could make this change [insert focus behavior here], where 1 is not at all confident and 10 is very confident?"

Follow up: "And why are you at a _____ [whatever number they stated] and not a _____ [lower number than they stated]?"

Then: "What strengths or skills do you have that might move you from a _____ to [higher number]?"

If importance and confidence are high, you might ask about commitment to change to evoke mobilizing change talk.

To evoke commitment:

Ask: "On a scale from 1 to 10, how committed are you to making this change [insert focus behavior here], where 1 is not at all committed and 10 is very committed?"

Follow up: "And why are you at a _____ [whatever number they stated] and not a _____ [lower number than they stated]?"

Then: "What ideas or next steps do you have that might move you from a _____ to [higher number]?"

USING CHANGE RULERS

· · · · · ·

Name: _____ Date: _____ Time: _____

On a scale of 1 to 10, with 1 being low and 10 being high, how *important* is it to you to _____

Not important at all   Somewhat important   Extremely important

1   2   3   4   5   6   7   8   9   10

Name: _____ Date: _____ Time: _____

On a scale of 1 to 10, with 1 being low and 10 being high, how *confident* are you that you could _____

Not confident at all confident   Somewhat confident   Extremely

1   2   3   4   5   6   7   8   9   10

Name: _____ Date: _____ Time: _____

On a scale of 1 to 10, with 1 being low and 10 being high, how *committed* are you to _____

Not committed at all   Somewhat committed   Extremely committed

1   2   3   4   5   6   7   8   9   10

The Change Thermometer

Change thermometers are a modification of the importance and confidence rulers to make them more concrete for people who have difficulty with abstract concepts. Thermometers convey the intensity of importance and confidence. Thermometers labeled with the person's change focus (Carey et al., 2007) help to underscore the meaning of greater and lesser intensity of "how important" and "how confident" a person feels about making a particular change. This makes it easier for the person to explore how the change is related to their priorities (e.g., "I just feel it's time to quit weed. I've been using too much. It's too expensive"). If the person has a variety of potential focuses for exploration, assigning a thermometer to each focus can help the person choose what focus they want to explore first.

CHANGE THERMOMETER

· · · · · ·

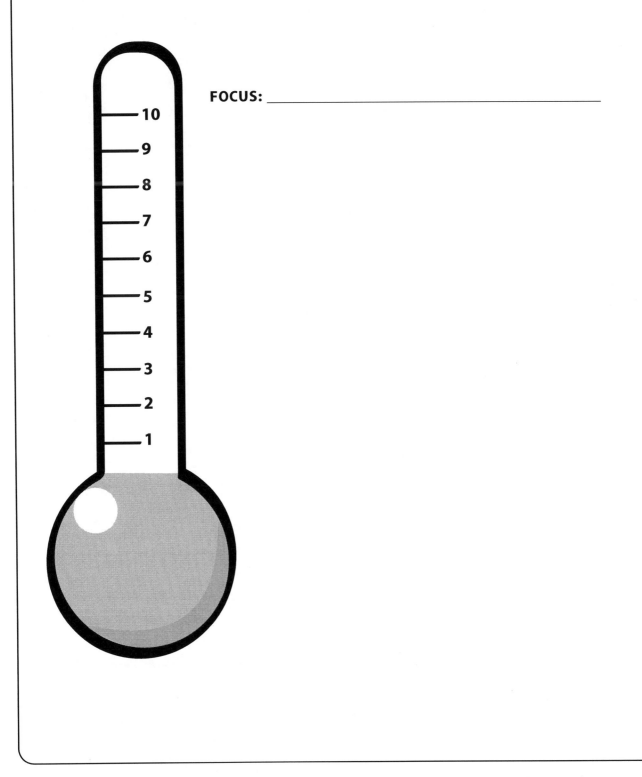

FOCUS: _____

A BRIDGE FOR CHANGE

This creative activity helps people envision the change they are considering, consider why it is important, and generate some concrete ideas about how they might want to cross the gap between where they are now and where they might want to be.

A BRIDGE FOR CHANGE

• • • • • •

Materials

- Large sheets of paper

- Markers, colored pencils, etc.

Instructions

Ask the person to imagine themselves standing on one side of a bridge that leads to the change they are contemplating on the other side:

- "What could the bridge to this change look like?"

- "Is it a bridge that strengthens the importance of the change or your confidence for making the change?"

- "How might we work together to build the bridge and strengthen your ability to get to this new place in your life?"

Invite them to draw a picture of a bridge. Ask them to put some "signs" on the near end of the bridge to represent where they are right now regarding a change. For example, someone who wants to feel less depressed might write:

- It's really, really hard.

- Two steps forward, three steps back.

- It feels really far away.

- I just want to feel better—this is really affecting my life.

Next, ask them to look at the other side of the bridge. What potential place of change do they see on the other side? What does that place look like?

Ask them to add signs on that side of the bridge that represent sights and experiences that characterize where they want to be, signs that represent new ways of thinking and feeling. Returning to our example of a person interested in feeling less depressed and more hopeful, they might say:

- "I feel so much better now that I don't have to worry about feeling tired so much anymore so my sign says, 'Energized.'"

- "I can think more clearly, sleep better and walk further, so my sign says, 'More powerful.'"

- "I'm out of the house more and spending more time with my friends, so my sign says, 'More social.'"

- "I feel different about myself, like my old self, but maybe even better, so my sign says, 'Feel better.'"

Ask the person to describe their guesses and hunches as to how they can bridge the gap between where they are now and where they want to be, and write them on the bridge. What are some of the raw materials they need to build their bridge? What information do they want to gather? What sorts of support might be helpful from you or others? For the person who wants to feel more hopeful and less depressed, some of these "raw materials" might look like:

- Social support and exercise: "I know my friend will walk with me every day, she's already doing it and wants me to join her. I need to think about my grandkids and having the energy to keep up with them. That will help me get out for the walk every morning."

- Self-affirmation: "I know all the reasons I should do it; I think it's how I think. Like I'm not important enough for this change. I think I need to talk to myself about how I am important and my feeling better is important. If I can convince myself I'm worth the effort, then I think I'll go ahead and do it."

- Medication: "I've used antidepressants before. I think I'd like to look into that again. It seemed to help last time."

And for strengthening confidence it might look like:

- Group: "My friend is having really good success talking about her feelings in the group. She says it makes it easier to cope because everyone offers ideas about what's working for them. And the check-in every week helps her stay honest about how she's really doing."

- Wake-up routine: "Every time I get out of bed on time I do better staying on track for the rest of the day. But when I feel really resentful or alone, it's harder to get out of bed. If I can figure out a way to get through that part, I think I'll be better able to stick to a healthier routine."

- Communication skills: "I need to figure out how to do this without my partner triggering me and making me mad. She gets really frustrated when I stay in bed. If I could talk to her about being a little more patient, I think I'll do better with getting up and getting going. Once I get mad at her, that's it, game over. It's all or nothing with me."

Finish the activity by summarizing the person's *most important* sustain talk and *all* of their change talk, and by identifying top priorities for next steps.

The Two Chairs Exercise

The purpose of the Two Chairs exercise is to offer the person a way to observe their ambivalence while they explore each side of it. This allows the person to focus on one side of their ambivalence at a time and explore thoughts, feelings, and beliefs about the change focus more deeply. As understanding deepens, the person becomes free to develop new ideas about how to move toward their goals.

To begin the exercise, set up two chairs across from one another. Next, you might introduce the exercise by inviting the person to consider having a friendly and understanding conversation with their own self from two different chairs. One chair might be a "stay where I am" chair, while the other is a "might change" chair.

You could invite the person to first sit in the "stay where I am" chair and ask them to speak about their perspective regarding the status quo. If the person wishes, they might speak directly to the (empty) "might change" chair. For example, consider a person who is feeling frustrated and stuck about household chores following a change in their partner's job and schedule. Exploration of "stay where I am" might sound something like this:

"I think I'm upset because my life feels really chaotic to me. My new job means my schedule is opposite from my partner's. When I'm at home, she's at work, and when she's at work, I'm at home. I've been spending most of my time at home taking care of the house and the lawn and buying groceries, etc. But when I come home from work there always seems to be something more that I have to do before I can relax. Lately I've been just letting it slide. There are always dishes in the sink now and neither of us is cleaning up or vacuuming. I don't like it. I want to come home, have something to eat, and relax, but I can't."

Next, you could invite the person to sit in the "might change" chair and speak from that point of view. If the person wishes, they might speak to the "stay where I am" chair. It might sound something like this:

"I guess, listening to myself, I see that I haven't tried just talking to her about it. I've been waiting until we have time together and that hasn't worked. I could try calling her when I'm on a break and ask if we could talk about something small…I don't know, the dishes in the sink, or sharing the grocery shopping. I guess I've been feeling like "if she loved me, she'd just do this and we wouldn't have to talk about it." But I know she's busy and stressed, she may not like it either and she might also feel stuck about what to do. Looking at it this way feels better to me, like we're in this together. I think I can talk to her about this and be less frustrated about everything. It's probably bothering her, too."

Here we see how the person's own observations of their ambivalence helped them generate some new ways of thinking about the situation and generate some ideas for ways to move forward. You may invite the person to switch chairs as often as they want, as long as the exercise seems productive. Summarize the most important remaining sustain talk and all the change talk and collaborate with the person on identifying their next steps.

"Yes, No, Maybe" Piles

This tool supports exploration of a person's reasons, ideas, and options for change using a structure whereby people literally sort through and organize their thoughts. To use this tool:

- Start by inviting the person to write down all their ideas, options, and reasons related to the change on sticky notes or pieces of paper.
- Next, invite them to sort their ideas, options, and reasons into three piles according to how helpful they are to them: a "yes" pile, a "maybe" pile, and a "no" pile.
- Invite them to talk about the ideas, options, and reasons in each pile and explore the considerations for each.
- Finally, summarize their most important remaining sustain talk and all of their change talk.

Figure 6 is an example of how one person might use this tool as they consider quitting smoking.

Yes	Maybe	No
I want to quit smoking.	Quit when I run out.	Quit cold turkey.
I need to quit for my health.	A group might help	Avoid people who are smoking.
Do something with my hands.	The patch might help.	Medication side effects.
Manage my anger.	Exercise might help.	Hypnosis.

Figure 6. Yes, Maybe, No

Decisional Balance: The Good Things and Less Good Things

The *decisional balance* (Sobell & Sobell, 1993) is a helpful way to structure a developing discrepancy conversation. The decisional balance supports our exploration of the good things and less good things about making a change and not making a change. We can add to this an exploration of how making the change relates to their goals and values. We use neutral language when we explore ambivalence to avoid generating discord. "Advantages" and "disadvantages" sound neutral in many conversations (e.g., whether or not to get a new job) and can be substituted with "good things" and "less good things" in other conversations. Remember to summarize the person's exploration after each question. An example of a completed decisional balancing exercise is in Figure 7.

Target Behavior: Medication	
No medication	**Taking medication**
Advantages	**Advantages**
I have more energy.	It's easier to get a job.
I lose weight.	The voices are quieter.
I feel my feelings.	Less relapse and hospitalization.
Disadvantages	**Disadvantages**
It's harder to concentrate.	I feel really tired all the time.
The voices are harder to ignore.	Drooling.
It's harder to pay attention at work.	Gaining weight.
My family worries about me more.	

Figure 7. Decisional Balance: Medication Adherence

DECISIONAL BALANCE

• • • • • •

Target Behavior: _____

Keeping the Behavior the Same	Making a Change
Advantages	**Advantages**
Disadvantages	**Disadvantages**

An alternative to using a grid is having the person write responses on separate index cards and then placing them in four piles (advantages of no change, disadvantages of no change, advantages of making a change, disadvantages of making a change). This can help people see the difference between large and small piles and explore their ambivalence.

Modified Decisional Balance

For some, simplifying the decisional balance reduces confusion and increases opportunities to evoke motivation. Martino et al. (2002) limit the questions to only the good things and not-so-good things about participating in treatment. Carey et al. (2007) offer the following tips for effective use of decisional balancing when people are likely to feel overwhelmed by the four questions:

- Increase positive expectations for the activity by describing it as something that people usually find helpful when making a decision.

- Offer to write down the person's responses so they can focus on their thoughts.

- Fold the four quadrants so only the top two sections are visible to reduce confusion and overwhelm.

- Take a break after completing the first two quadrants to help maintain interest and reduce fatigue. Also, consider doing the exercise over two conversations, completing two quadrants each time.

- Review the person's responses to the first two quadrants before moving on to the next two quadrants to refresh the person's memory and ground the activity.

Caveats to Decisional Balancing

There are situations in which use of the decisional balance tool is inappropriate. For example:

- The decisional balance is not recommended as a way to resolve ambivalence when the person is already offering change talk. The sustain talk brought forward during the decisional balance can intensify the person's ambivalence about making the change and reduce the likelihood that they will commit to the change (Miller & Rose, 2015).

- The decisional balance is also not recommended when a person minimizes the need for a change because they feel unable to otherwise cope with a difficult situation. When people are in situations that feel impossible or overwhelming, it is important to understand and accept their perception of the situation. We might instead choose to bring forward the person's strengths, skills, and resources and then, as they are willing, evoke their change talk and their ideas and options for success if they were to decide to make a change.

- The decisional balance may be a helpful way to support a person in further strengthening their commitment to make a change after the person has already committed to make that change (Miller & Rose, 2015).

Pathways to Change

Pathways to change is a structured way to have an equipoise conversation with a person who is struggling to decide on a particular change direction (Nashölm, 2006). While remaining neutral, we structure the exploration of the person's perspective by exploring current and new directions as separate *pathways* to their goals.

As we listen to how they describe the path they are on and their dilemma, we might ask them to envision a pathway that represents the path they are currently traveling (i.e., their current situation) and the crossroad (i.e., their dilemma or the decision they face). We might invite them to label the path they are currently on (e.g., "no change") and the crossroads (e.g., "I need a better job"). This exploration might lead to identifying multiple change pathways they might take to reach their goal:

- We can invite the person to name and describe the paths as they branch to the left, to the right, or to the middle, exploring the person's perspective and experience of their situation.

- As they describe what it might be like to travel down each path, explore the good and less good things about each path.

- Invite them to imagine meeting themselves down each of these paths sometime in the future. Ask them what that would be like and how they would see themselves in the future.

In considering all these possibilities, the person may even decide to forge a new path or decide that they want to combine two paths instead of traveling only one. As a more visual alternative, you could have the person actually draw and label pathways on a large sheet of paper.

EXPLORING PATHWAYS

• • • • • •

Stay on Current Path (Briefly Describe)	Alternate Path 1 (Briefly Describe)	Alternate Path 2 (Briefly Describe)
Good Things	Good Things	Good Things
Less Good Things	Less Good Things	Less Good Things

MULTIPLE PATHWAYS TO CHANGE

• • • • • •

Let's revisit Ruby, the mom in Chapter 2 who feels stuck as she tries to decide whether to move into the subsidized apartment with her partner and child:

Ruby is diagnosed with a serious and chronic mental health issue. She is living with her partner and child. Although they have a place to live, Ruby is barely managing to stretch her income to pay the rent and bills. They are right on the cusp of being homeless. She tells you that her partner is the source of her pain and struggle. The partner spends their time playing video games and does not contribute to the household upkeep and expenses. Ruby is often moved to tears as she expresses her frustration. Recently, the partner asked Ruby to move into a new subsidized apartment, but there is a catch. The partner would have to be the only identified renter because if Ruby were also on the lease, the apartment would be too expensive. Ruby has two months to decide whether to stay in her current apartment (with her child and without the partner) or for both of them to move in with the partner.

How would you ask permission to explore her situation using the multiple pathways approach?

_____

_____

_____

_____

_____

How would you invite her to label the different pathways to her decision?

_____

_____

_____

_____

_____

What labels might she use for "Stay on Current Path," "Alternative Path 1," and "Alternative Path 2?"

_____

_____

_____

_____

Imagine that she chooses the following labels:

- "Stay in our apartment (mom and child)."

- "Find a less expensive apartment."

- "Move into his subsidized apartment."

Using the Exploring Pathways tool described earlier, how might she describe the good things and less good things about each of these three situations?

The good things and less good things about staying in her apartment (mom and child):

_____

_____

_____

_____

The good things and less good things about getting a less expensive apartment with her child:

_____

_____

_____

_____

The good things and less good things about moving into her partner's apartment:

_____

_____

_____

_____

Now practice how you might use *summaries* to pull together what she has said and reflect back her perceptions of the situation.

Summarize the good things and less good things about staying in her current apartment (mom and child):

_____

_____

_____

_____

Summarize the good things and less good things about getting a less expensive apartment with her child:

_____

_____

_____

_____

Summarize the good things and less good things about moving into her partner's subsidized apartment:

_____

_____

_____

_____

_____

What do you notice about your understanding of Ruby's perspective and dilemma as she explores the current situation, keeping things the same, and change?

_____

_____

_____

_____

How might Ruby's exploration of her situation help her identify what she wants to do next?

_____

_____

_____

_____

THE DANCE OF MI: FROM EVOKING TO PLANNING

As the person decides they are ready to work on a plan for change, we guide the conversation toward the planning process and help them sort their options and create a plan. They should develop confidence that a plan can work for them and that they can commit to carrying out the plan.

Signals to Increase Evoking

- The person's ambivalence about making the change is not resolving.
- The person is not identifying reasons and need for change.
- The person is not able to envision making the change.

Practitioner Strategies for Increasing Evoking

Try the following strategies to evoke change talk and consider whether the conversation needs to be refocused to address the person's dilemma:

- Hold the focus steady. Summarize the person's most important sustain talk and *all* of their change talk about importance and confidence.
- Seek to understand the person's priorities and any dilemmas underlying the importance of the change and the person's confidence for making the change. Explore whether the person wants to shift to a new change focus, perhaps to an easier change for an early win and confidence boost before making a more ambitious change.
- Normalize the difficulty of the change process.
- Emphasize the person's right to choose the change focus and how to change.
- Affirm the person's values, strengths, and intentions based on what they've already said and related to the change focus.
- Consider whether to explore the person's ambivalence with neutrality (i.e., good things and less good things about their current situation, keeping things the same in the future, and making the change).
- Avoid persuading the person to change, using confrontation, asking too many questions, and offering unsolicited advice, information, suggestions.

Signals to Guide Toward Planning

- The person is doing most of the talking, thoughtfully exploring a specific change focus and is looking ahead to future benefits of change or envisioning barriers that need to be addressed to make the change.
- The person's exploration may be starting to uncover their own good ideas about how they might make the change and when they might start.
- The person's ambivalence about making the change is resolving and they are expressing intention to make the change in the near future.

Practitioner Strategies to Guide Toward Planning

- Check accurate understanding by summarizing all the person's change talk, their most important remaining sustain talk, and any decisions and commitments for the change focus.

- Reflect emerging next steps from the person's perspective and explore their ideas specifically and concretely.

- If the options for change planning are limited, offer choices for how to proceed (e.g., menu of options).

- Explore and increase importance, confidence, and commitment for change.

- Explore the person's ideas for backup plans and "if-then" plans.

- Avoid taking over and prescribing a plan.

CHAPTER SUMMARY

· · · · · ·

What do you see as the most important points of this chapter?

_____

_____

_____

_____

_____

What interested you the most?

_____

_____

_____

_____

_____

What focusing strategies are you most likely to try?

_____

_____

_____

_____

_____

8

PLANNING: THE BRIDGE TO CHANGE

A goal without a plan is just a wish.
—Antoine de Saint-Exupéry

IN THIS CHAPTER

- Testing the Water for Planning
- Sample Initial Planning Conversation
- Strengthening Commitment for Making a Change
- Moving from "Why" to "How": Action Planning
- Resolving Ambivalence While Creating a Plan
- Tools to Enhance Following Through and Sustaining Change
- The Dance of MI: From Planning to Preventing Recurrence

The planning process follows evocation of the person's importance and confidence for making a change. Plans are tailored to the person's goals and ideas for change appropriate to their readiness. Some plans have preliminary process steps designed to increase importance or confidence for making a change. Other plans are appropriate for navigating the change itself, and still others address potential barriers to maintaining a change (e.g., if–then plans). Subsequent sessions revise plans based on the person's progress, motivation, and commitment to making the change. In this chapter, we will explore developing effective MI-consistent plans.

A common challenge in planning emerges when we ask about next steps before we have resolved enough of the person's dilemma about making a change for them to be able to generate ideas for a plan. In the following exchange, the focus seems clear until the person's dilemma about change comes into sharper focus.

Person: "I'd like to feel safer when I walk to the grocery store."

Practitioner [prematurely testing for planning]: "What thoughts do you have about how you could feel safer?"

Person: "I don't know, I only feel safe in my house, and I still get panic attacks even when I'm home. Weed is the only thing that keeps me from feeling like I'm going to totally lose my mind. Maybe I should just keep smoking weed and stay home."

Premature planning intensifies ambivalence and increases the likelihood the person will decide to postpone making a change. We may feel tempted to prescribe a change plan when we work within a setting that has predetermined recommendations or a service package. To create plans that incorporate the person's intrinsic motivation, we want to ensure that we've explored the person's *why* and *can* for change, before negotiating the *how*.

TESTING THE WATER FOR PLANNING

Making the transition into planning involves recognizing the person's readiness to negotiate a change plan. Testing the water makes it easier to see the person's readiness signals:

- Sustain talk becomes less frequent.
- Change talk increases in strength and frequency.
- Mobilizing change talk is emerging (e.g., "It's time for me to quit smoking," "I need to feel less depressed because I need to get a job," "I've been wondering about whether meditation works for anxiety").
- Envisioning increases (e.g., "If I did this, it would be easier to…").
- Commitment talk increases in strength and frequency (e.g., "I'm going to…").

To test the water, we use a *transitional summary* of the person's most important remaining sustain talk and all of their change talk. This consolidates the person's exploration and checks whether it is the time to begin planning. Transitional summaries:

- Begin with a statement indicating that you are making a summary ("Let me see if I understand so far," "Here is what I've heard. Tell me if I've missed anything").
- If the person is "feeling two ways" about changing, name both sides of the ambivalence in the summary ("On the one hand you…, on the other hand…").
- Highlight the person's change talk thus far ("You mentioned several reasons why you would want to make this change, including…").
- End with an invitation ("What would you add?").

Here is an example of a transitional summary that pulls all of these steps together.

Let me see if I understand where we are so far. It's really important to you to feel safer in your home and on the street. You see how it will help your health and your happiness, and that's important to you. You've used the grounding techniques off and on for the past few weeks, and those seem to help sometimes. Lately you've been using weed more to feel comfortable especially when the panic attacks feel really intense. There are things about weed that you don't like—how it sometimes makes you feel more anxious and your concerns about smoking and your health. Your panic attacks are worse since the recent shootings in your neighborhood and may be related to some experiences you had when you were younger. You are wondering if there are other things you can do to address the panic attacks and those earlier experiences to see if that helps you feel safer. What have I missed?

SAMPLE INITIAL PLANNING CONVERSATION

Let's take a look at an initial planning conversation with Leona.

> **Practitioner:** "You want to find a way to cope with the anxiety and panic attacks, improve your sleep and your mornings, and eventually taper off the medication. Knowing what to expect, having someone to talk to, those are both things that help. What else?"

> **Leona:** "Having something to do that works. So I don't feel so desperate or like I'm going crazy or going to die? So I have some control?"

> **Practitioner:** "That makes sense. You've mentioned a few things that are happening: irritability, heart pounding, shortness of breath, fear … What do you know about what people do to manage that kind of intense anxiety?"

> **Leona:** "Well, I don't know, yoga? Meditation?"

> **Practitioner:** "Sure, those are things people have used. What are your thoughts about how those might work for you?"

> **Leona:** "I tried a meditation class once; I'd do that. Does that really work?"

> **Practitioner:** "Yes, it can be helpful. Is it alright if I mention some other options as well?"

> **Leona:** "Sure."

> **Practitioner:** "Different things work better for different people so you will know best where we should start. Some things we might consider are breathing exercises that can help with the shortness of breath. Progressive muscle relaxation can help with the anxiety, and mindfulness can help with feeling disconnected and fuzzy. Gentle exercise is often helpful, and changing negative thoughts helps with things like feeling as if you might be going crazy or about to die. Given those options, what sounds like it might be a good fit for you?"

> **Leona:** "I'd like something that makes me feel better fast. Can the breathing and relaxation make me feel better fast?"

> **Practitioner:** "Yes, people find it helpful to practice those so they can catch the anxiety right when it starts and stop it in its tracks."

> **Leona:** "Okay, can we start with that today?"

> **Practitioner:** "Sure; so one thing we'll do together today is to talk about using simple breathing exercises and progressive muscle relaxation to decrease the intensity of the anxiety. What else do you think would be helpful?"

> **Leona:** "I think I need to talk to my doctor about waiting before starting the taper and making it a really gradual taper. Do you really think she'll be willing to consider that? Will you help me talk to her?"

> **Practitioner:** "I'm happy to work with both of you to make sure we are all on the same page and working together to manage your panic attacks and make this taper successful. So we have

the breathing, the relaxation, the call with your doctor. What else might help to support your success?"

Leona: "You know, the worst is the unpredictability, I'll be in the grocery store or a meeting and 'bam' all I can do is get out of there as fast as possible."

Practitioner: "So it's especially hard to manage it when it surprises you."

Leona: "Yes, that's it. Does anything help with that?"

Practitioner: "Well, the breathing and relaxation can help with that. Some people feel that journaling actually relieves some of the fear, too. It's hard to remember the surprising or especially difficult experiences afterward and a journal allows you to look back and see the experiences you've already made it through. People say it helps with that feeling of it being especially scary. But I don't know if that is something that would interest you."

Journaling is a concrete way for a person to measure progress toward their goals. A journal can:

- Provide a space for envisioning in detail how life will be even better, further boosting motivation for persisting toward goals.

- Help monitor how a change is going and indicate when a person may need more support (e.g., agreeing to contact the practitioner if their mood is particularly low two days in a row).

- Help boost confidence for making a change by tracking successes a person can look back on at a time when they feel discouraged (a sort of "survival guide").

Leona: "I guess it makes sense that I may not remember that I've already been through something like that before. So how would I do that? Just write it down and go back over it when I'm really anxious?"

Practitioner: "Some people find it really helpful."

Leona: "Well I guess it can't hurt. It might be helpful to have it to look back on."

Practitioner: "Like your own custom-made survival guide."

Leona: "Yeah, I guess so."

Practitioner: "So it sounds like you might want to start today with learning some breathing and progressive muscle relaxation and beginning to journal your experiences."

Leona: "Yeah and finding a time to talk with my doctor about waiting until I can manage my panic attacks and then a really gradual taper. Can we do that? Can we call together today?"

Practitioner: "Yes, I think that makes a lot of sense. So, let me just make sure we have a plan worked out that makes sense to you. You are doing your best to take good care of your kids, do your work, and manage your anxiety. You are willing to work on strategies to manage the anxiety and panic you feel to get ready to gradually taper off the medication. You are interested in talking together with your doctor about a plan to wait a bit and then taper down gradually and keep the taper manageable. To start managing the anxiety you are having now, you want to start practicing some breathing and progressive muscle relaxation when you feel the anxiety start to intensify. You are also interested in starting a journal to help track your progress and have a record of the experiences you can look back on for reassurance when the panic attacks feel particularly challenging. Is that right? Is that what you want to do?"

Leona: "Well I don't have much of a choice, do I? I'm not looking forward to this. But I see how more medication won't help, you know, in the long run. I'm really wishing that was an option for now..."

Practitioner: "You aren't looking forward to this and at the same time you sound like you are willing to give it a try."

Leona: "Is that okay?"

Practitioner: "It's really normal to feel uncomfortable with this kind of change. What do you think will help you stay on track with this, especially when you start feeling really uncomfortable?"

Leona: "That isn't going to be easy, but I'm going to try that breathing and relaxation. I'm not a big fan of medication in the first place. I need this to work. I just want to get back to being myself again, for me and the kids."

Practitioner: "You see how this can help you make an even better life for yourself and your kids. You want to find a way to be successful with this. So, if you are ready, what do you think we should do first?"

Leona: "Can we call my doctor first? I'm most anxious about that."

Practitioner: "Okay, we'll make the call first and then practice breathing and progressive relaxation. When we're done, I can give you an app to help with practicing at home if you feel like that will be helpful. What do you think?"

Leona: "Yes, let's do it!"

The session continues with the call to Leona's doctor and breathing/relaxation practice.

Practitioner: "Leona, it seems like you really got the way the breathing and progressive relaxation works! So, what do you think will help you get a strong start with managing your anxiety and panic attacks over the next few weeks? Where do you want to start?"

Leona: "Well, I think I want to use the breathing and relaxation we practiced, and the journal."

Practitioner: "Okay, so what might help you to remember to use the breathing?"

Leona: "Every day?"

Practitioner: "If you can; daily practice usually helps people master a breathing exercise so they can use it effectively when they feel anxious or panicky."

Leona: "Well, I could probably do it every morning when I get up and feel irritable. And also when I feel a panic attack coming on."

Practitioner: "Okay, so you'll practice when you wake up and whenever you feel panicky. What about the relaxation, when would you practice that?"

Leona: "Well, I could practice the relaxation when I'm in bed instead of watching the clock on my phone and videos and stuff, and whenever I feel anxious?"

Practitioner: "So your plan is to practice breathing when you wake up and when you feel panicky and relaxation when you go to bed and when you feel anxious."

INITIAL PLANNING

· · · · · ·

How might you summarize Leona's initial plan for the next few weeks, including her top three objectives?

_____

_____

_____

_____

What MI skills did the practitioner use to guide Leona in creating an initial plan?

_____

_____

_____

_____

What tools or strategies could you have used in a planning conversation?

_____

_____

_____

_____

STRENGTHENING COMMITMENT FOR MAKING A CHANGE

During the planning process, we attend to confidence and commitment language in the same way we strengthened importance and confidence during the evoking phase. We want to recognize commitment language when we hear it because it is one of our signals to know if we are guiding in the direction of initiating a change. Commitment language differs from change talk in that it signals a certain level of *intention* to take some action. Commitment language ranges from low commitment strength to high commitment strength (Amrhein et al., 2003).

Low-strength commitment language sounds like:

- "I'll try to take my medications as prescribed."
- "I hope to take my medications as prescribed."
- "I agree to take my medications as prescribed."

High-strength commitment language sounds like:

- "I will take my medications as prescribed."
- "I'm determined to take my medications as prescribed."
- "I promise I'll take my medications as prescribed."

When the person's commitment language increases in frequency and strength from the beginning of the conversation to the end, we know we're more likely to be guiding in the direction of change. When confidence and commitment strength are low, we use more reflections, affirmations, and evocative questions to strengthen the person's exploration of options for initiating the change (Martin, Christopher, Houck, & Moyers, 2011).

RATING COMMITMENT STRENGTH

· · · · · ·

This exercise is an opportunity to practice recognizing the strength of different commitment statements. Recognizing commitment strength makes it easier to guide conversations during the planning process. Rate each of the following statements from 1 to 5 in terms of their commitment strength, with 1 representing low commitment strength and 5 representing high commitment strength.

_____ 1. I'll think about this weight loss stuff and let you know what I decide.

_____ 2. Fruits and vegetables are expensive. I need some low-cost options I can afford.

_____ 3. I know the grounding techniques help. I'll try to use them; the anxiety just gets so strong so fast.

_____ 4. I agree that I feel better when I eat well.

_____ 5. I'm going to walk some every day. I think it will help my mood.

_____ 6. I plan to keep a journal so we can talk about my thoughts and feelings during the week. I think that will help me understand what's holding me back.

_____ 7. I might try the diet; it's just hard to take it seriously.

_____ 8. Maybe I could try to eat breakfast; then I might eat better later in the day, too.

_____ 9. I already lost two pounds since we last talked.

_____ 10. I feel fine, but I'll think about what you've told me.

_____ 11. I will make sure to drink a glass of water with my meals; that will curb the hunger.

_____ 12. If it gets bad, I'll just call the suicide hotline. No more medication for me.

_____ 13. I'm trying, but it's so hard with all these food restrictions.

_____ 14. I think I can walk twice a week with my partner; she's a good support for me.

_____ 15. I will walk tomorrow.

_____ 16. I said "no" to some voices yesterday. I think I can do it again tomorrow, too.

_____ 17. I know I should take this stuff seriously. I just don't know how.

_____ 18. I'll do some small things to see my friends. I'll start by emailing my best friend about a good time to talk.

_____ 19. This is really getting serious. I'm committed to being a good role model for my kids.

_____ 20. I think I'm ready to make some changes.

_____ 21. I can try to not binge eat, but really, I'm not usually able to stop. It's the only thing I want to do after everyone else is in bed.

_____ 22. I'm already starting to walk 10,000 steps a day, and I'm feeling better about myself.

_____ 23. I'm going to do this.

MOVING FROM "WHY" TO "HOW": ACTION PLANNING

How do we facilitate a person's transition from *thinking* about change to actually *doing* things to initiate the change? What about when they are expressing some difficulty with follow-through? For example, we often hear things like:

- "I know I could take my medications more regularly."
- "I meant to take them daily."
- "I tried earlier this week to get a ride to pick up my refill."
- "I think I would feel better if I could just take my medication regularly."
- "I just forget."

Facilitating a person's transition to taking action includes:

- Eliciting the person's own ideas and knowledge about the subject: "What have you heard about how people get support to stop using substances?" or "What ideas do you have for transportation?"

- Offering information and advice in an MI-consistent way (see Chapter 4). During the planning process, it is helpful to have some ideas about what might help the person reach their goal.

- Seeking collaboration to bring forward the person's expertise and wisdom about how the information or advice might work for them: "What are your thoughts about these ideas for your situation?" or "How might these ideas work for you?"

- Emphasizing autonomy, or freedom of choice, in deciding what they want to do with the advice: "A lot of people find that *x* works well, but I don't know if that's something that interests you" or "It's your decision what you choose to do; you are the expert on what will work for you."

The Solutions Chair

One construct that supports autonomy is the notion of the *solutions chair*. The changes that people make spring from the ideas and resources that they bring forward or support. When we believe that people already have the necessary resources and expertise to make changes in their lives, we are more likely to talk with them in ways that facilitate activation of those resources. You could ask a person to actually visualize sitting in *their* "solutions chair" (or use an actual chair) during the discussion. When we invite them to sit in their chair, they are more likely to verbalize their resources for change (i.e., priorities, reasons, options, values, and ideas for change; see Figure 8). When they verbalize these resources, it is more likely that they will make a change and stick with it.

After eliciting a person's own ideas, we may ask permission to offer additional ideas if it seems necessary, making sure to again bring forth the person's own ideas about how they may or may not *use* these ideas. All change takes place from the position of the solutions chair—so we want the person to talk from it early and often.

The Solutions Chair...

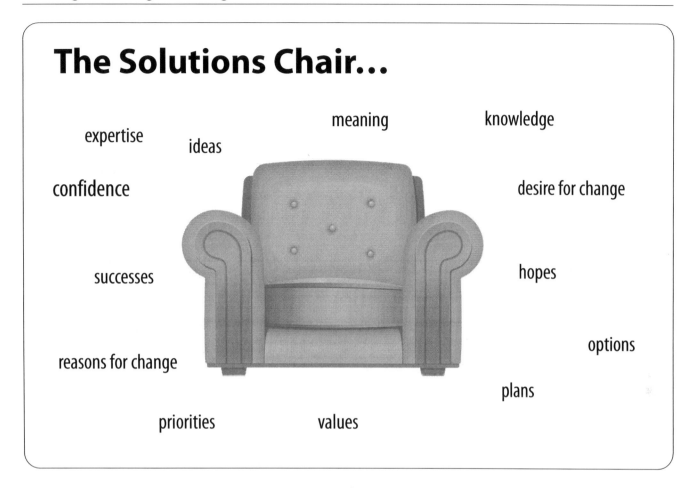

expertise   ideas   meaning   knowledge

confidence   desire for change

successes   hopes

options

reasons for change

plans

priorities   values

Using Reflections for Planning

Action reflections highlight the person's own motivations for change. Action reflections guide toward change activation by focusing on the person's autonomy and their ideas for the how, when, and where to change. Action reflections contain both specific steps the person has already mentioned and the practitioner's sense of where the person seems to be going. The following are some examples of action reflections (Resnicow & McMaster, 2012):

Omission reflections highlight ideas or solutions the person has not raised, which seem like intentional omissions: "I notice you didn't mention *x, y, z*, which seems like a natural solution for you, so I assume you've already decided it won't work for you" or "It seems likely that you've already considered *x* and are wondering whether it would work for you in this situation."

Barrier flipping reflections shine a light on the person's interest in options to *overcome* obstacles to change: "In order to move forward, it sounds like you are wondering how to address barriers *x, y,* and *z.*"

General next step reflections highlight the person's own nonspecific ideas for next steps (e.g., coping with cravings, medication, changing routine) to explore specific strategies for the next steps: "So you might consider doing something like *x, y,* or *z.*"

Specific next step reflections highlight the person's own (implicit or explicit) specific strategy preferences: "It sounds like doing *x* is a possibility" or "You're starting to think *x* is a good possibility" or "Given that *x* seems comfortable for you, that might be a great option for you here."

Reframing perception reflections highlight a potential way to view the change that increases the person's options, competence, or ability to make the change: "In order to move forward, you're beginning to think of ways to view this differently" or "You're wondering if it's time to view this differently." Another variation on this reflection is to reframe the person's past change efforts to highlight their experience: "Knowing you've been successful with things like this in the past is going to help you think through this challenge" or "Knowing what this is like, you're starting to think of new ways…"

The Why, How, When, and Where of Change

Another way we facilitate the change planning process is by having the person come up with examples that speak to the *why, how, when,* and *where* of change. Specifics for implementing a challenging change plan increase the likelihood that the person will follow through. In the end, the change plan should show the relationship between the person's goals, strengths, resources, and next steps. A change plan should include actions the person will take on their own and specific interventions the person will participate in during treatment. The Change Plan Worksheet (Ingersoll, Wagner, & Gahrib, 2002) offers 10 helpful prompts to guide a person in developing a plan for change. When using the Change Plan Worksheet, we invite the person to fill in the worksheet, or if they prefer, we fill it in according to their answers. As the person creates their plan, we use our EARS to guide the process and strengthen their commitment.

Once the worksheet is completed, we can consolidate the person's commitment to the plan by asking the following questions:

- "Is this something you are willing to commit to?" (we may want to use a commitment change ruler or thermometer)
- "What else might get in your way?"
- "What else needs to be added or removed from your plan to make it 100 percent doable?"

THE CHANGE PLAN WORKSHEET

· · · · · ·

The change I want to make:

_____

_____

_____

_____

_____

The reasons I want to make this change:

_____

_____

_____

_____

_____

My skills and abilities (including what I am already doing well in this area, as well as past or other successes) to make this change:

_____

_____

_____

_____

_____

The steps I plan to take to make this change:

_____

_____

_____

_____

_____

The ways others can help me make this change:

_____

_____

_____

_____

_____

When I will start to make this change:

_____

_____

_____

_____

_____

How I will prepare to start making this change:

_____

_____

_____

_____

_____

How I will know if my plan is working:

_____

_____

_____

_____

Challenges that might interfere with my plan:

_____

_____

_____

_____

What I will do if the plan isn't working:

_____

_____

_____

_____

Source: Ingersoll, Wagner, & Gharib, 2002.

USING THE CHANGE PLAN WORKSHEET

· · · · · ·

Invite a friend or colleague to talk to you about something they *want* to change, *can* change, and are *thinking about changing* but haven't started yet. Use the Change Plan Worksheet to guide the discussion. At the end of the conversation, ask your partner about the strength of their commitment and what was most helpful to them in making their plan. Remember to use your EARS to guide their exploration of each question.

When you explore potential next steps, guide toward steps that are rewarding *and* will help your partner make progress toward their change goal. Remember to seek collaboration and emphasize autonomy, especially when offering information or advice.

When you have finished, you may want to debrief with your partner by asking about the process. For example: "What was this exercise like for you?" "Did you feel supported in creating your plan?" "Is there any way I could have been more helpful to you?"

SMART Planning

At some point, your employer or an insurer will expect a written plan, typically a SMART (**S**pecific, **M**easurable, **A**chievable, **R**ealistic, and **T**ime-limited) plan. And the people with whom you work will want a tangible plan as a daily reminder of what they are doing to reach their goals. A good SMART plan maps out a person's intentions in a measurable and manageable way. It can build on and refine the work done in the Change Plan Worksheet.

Figure 9 is an example of a plan designed with Leona to increase her capacity to reach her long-term goals. By design, the plan removes barriers to her goals using her preferred activities and important relationships, roles, health-related activities, and treatment interventions to help her taper off the alprazolam.

Name: Leona Bender   **Date: June 20, 2020**

Goal:
I want to feel happy, hopeful, and productive again.

Strengths and Resources:
- Committed to her children's well-being and happiness.
- Significant determination and self-control.
- Willing to call Sheila when she needs to talk about her day and ask for an occasional break.
- Values her self-care and already knows effective ways to take care of herself.
- Specific goals already identified: improving sleep routine, improving morning routine, eating healthy meals, restarting exercise routine, learning new strategies to manage anxiety and panic

Potential Barriers:
- Chaotic daily schedule makes it harder to get the kids up on time, get enough sleep, eat healthy meals, and have time for exercise and play.
- Wants more strategies for coping with anxiety and panic.

Objective 1:
Leona will practice self-care strategies at least once a day for the next 4 weeks.

Objective 1 Interventions

Person Responsible and Intervention	Intensity	Frequency	Duration
Leona will reestablish a regular bedtime routine with the kids.	n/a	5x/wk	3 mos
Leona will establish a regular bedtime routine for herself.	n/a	5x/wk	w/in 4 wks
Sheila will talk with her on the phone to provide support and take care of the kids occasionally when she needs a break.	n/a	3x/wk	6 mos
Leona will enroll in a healthy meals delivery program to make it easier to prepare healthy meals.	n/a	1x	w/in 4 wks

Objective 2:
Leona will try out three new strategies in the next month to cope with anxiety as evidenced by self-report.

Objective 2 Interventions

Person Responsible and Intervention	Intensity	Frequency	Duration
Anna B., LCSW, will provide 1:1 CBT to assist with anxiety management and coping with panic attacks.	45 min	1x/wk	6 mos
Leona will attend meditation practice sessions by Jill D., to create a routine practice and provide opportunities to socialize.	60 min	1x/wk	4 wks
Leona will practice deep breathing in a.m. to reduce irritability.	n/a	5x/wk	4 wks
Leona will practice progressive muscle relaxation in p.m. to reduce anxiety.	n/a	5x/wk	4 wks
Leona will go for a walk with the kids or play a game.	n/a	2x/wk	3 mos

Objective 3:
Within 30 days Leona will be ready to start a gradual taper from alprazolam as measured by self-report.

Objective 3 Interventions

Person Responsible and Intervention	Intensity	Frequency	Duration
Dr. A will provide medical supervision of a gradual taper for the purpose of decreasing withdrawal symptoms and increasing capacity to establish a regular self-care routine, manage anxiety symptoms with new coping skills, and increase productivity.	15 min	2x/mo	3 mos
Leona will maintain a journal of her anxiety and panic and review it in therapy to identify triggers and learn coping strategies to manage withdrawal symptoms.	30 min	5x/wk	6 mos

Figure 9. Leona's SMART Plan

SMART PLAN TEMPLATE

· · · · · ·

Name:	Date:

Goal:

Strengths and Resources:

Potential Barriers:

Objective 1:

Objective 1 Interventions

Person Responsible and Intervention	Intensity	Frequency	Duration

Objective 2:			
Objective 2 Interventions			
Person Responsible and Intervention	*Intensity*	*Frequency*	*Duration*

Objective 3:			
Objective 3 Interventions			
Person Responsible and Intervention	*Intensity*	*Frequency*	*Duration*

RESOLVING AMBIVALENCE WHILE CREATING A PLAN

We may hear what sounds like strong commitment speech early in the change process, and then the person's sustain talk may intensify in the midst of creating the plan. When this happens, we respond flexibly using our EARS and if necessary move back into evoking to soften sustain talk and build change talk until the person is again ready to move into planning. Sometimes this exploration reveals that the person's confidence for making the change is low and they are having a hard time envisioning how they could make the change. It can be helpful in these circumstances to go back to focusing and refocus on an *early win* (see Chapter 6). The momentum from evoking, planning, and accomplishing an early win can boost the person's confidence and readiness to take on more ambitious change goals.

What do we do when people aren't ready to take action steps on their most important goals and need to build functioning? We can create a *discovery plan* that helps the person build functioning and resolve ambivalence for change. Figure 10 shows the flow of planning to resolve ambivalence.

Discovery Planning: Process Steps

Just as we explore hypothetical ways a person might make a change during the evoking phase, we can work with the person to create the *next steps* that increase their functioning and explore their importance, confidence, and readiness for change. Next steps for building functioning and resolving ambivalence can be called *process steps* and are designed to increase readiness for specific desired changes. Process steps should be the most ambitious next steps the person can manage given their

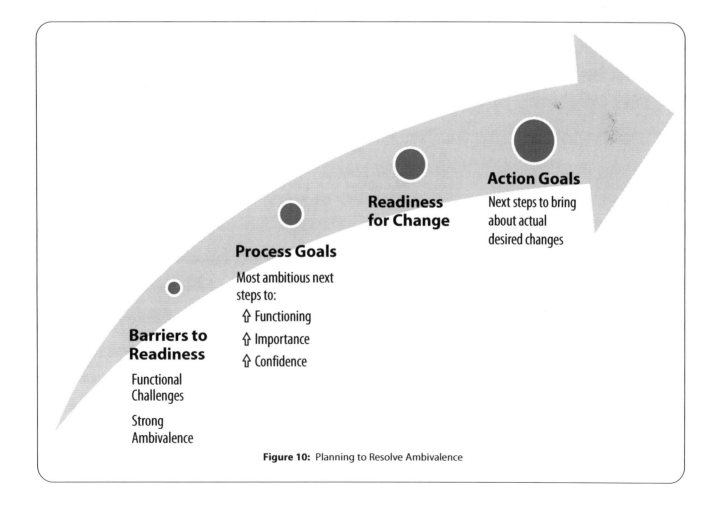

Action Goals

Next steps to bring about actual desired changes

Readiness for Change

Process Goals

Most ambitious next steps to:

⇧ Functioning

⇧ Importance

⇧ Confidence

Barriers to Readiness

Functional Challenges

Strong Ambivalence

Figure 10: Planning to Resolve Ambivalence

readiness, functioning, symptom severity, and environmental conditions (Tondora, 2013). We work together to identify specific, concrete, ambitious steps that are attainable in a relatively short period of time that support the person's momentum toward achieving their most important goals. Process steps:

- Address or resolve goal-specific barriers and challenges.
- Demonstrate measurable progress (i.e., we can agree yes or no that the step was completed).
- Apply the person's values, life goals, strengths, skills, intentions, and resources.
- Specify time, frequency, and duration.

Process steps are scaffolded to strengthen functioning. We start by asking, "What are some specific next steps to help you achieve [life goals]? What would you be able to do in the next four weeks that would help you make progress toward your goals?" Here is an example of a person's attainable and measurable process steps scaffolded to help the person increase their functioning and develop momentum toward their goals (Tondora, 2013):
"I want to…"

- Be able to get out of bed by 9 a.m. at least four days out of five (M–F).
- Apply for SSDI on the telephone on [specific date].
- Demonstrate three mood management skills per week in the next 30 days.
- Attend a minimum of one church activity weekly over the next 90 days.
- Complete a job résumé within three months.
- Work five hours in the community within six months.

When people are strongly ambivalent about the *importance* of a change, we can identify process steps to explore the person's reasons for making the change. For example:
"I want to…"

- Calculate my total lifetime spending on cigarettes.
- Identify at least two adverse effects of substance use on my well-being.
- Identify three benefits of taking medications on my mood.

Similarly, when *ability* and *confidence* to make a change are low, we can identify process steps that explore how they might make the change if they choose to do so. During these conversations, it is common to discover "blind spots" in the person's understanding, and it is helpful to offer information with permission (Carey et al., 2007):

Jamal: "Well, I think my voices get worse because I forget to take my meds and I watch TV all day."

Practitioner: "So that's when you feel pretty out of it."

Jamal: "Yeah, there's really nothing to do."

Practitioner: "Tell me more about what you do while you watch TV."

Jamal: "Nothing really, if there's beer I'll drink it."

Practitioner: "So you forget your meds and watch TV. Sounds like you feel pretty bored, and that's when you might have beer."

Jamal: "Yeah."

Practitioner: "What do you know about how beer can affect hearing voices?"

Jamal: "What do you mean?"

Practitioner: "People generally find that alcohol makes their voices worse. How might that be for you?"

Jamal: "I don't know. I didn't know that could happen."

Practitioner: "So that's a surprise to you. What do you think about us working together on ways to remember to take your medications and ways you could cut down or quit drinking beer?"

Jamal: "Well, it sounds like that could help. I'd like to not feel so bored."

Hypothetical Plans for Change: Generalizing Skills

In addition to a here-and-now change plan, we may find ourselves helping a person develop a hypothetical plan for change. A hypothetical change plan can generalize skills needed in a person's current situation into go-to capacities for future environments and challenges (e.g., transitioning outside an institution, moving into the next phases of treatment, getting a challenging new job, the end of a relationship). Preferably there will be opportunities for practicing in the moment the skills, strengths, and values needed to translate to successes in the larger world. Consider Carl:

Carl had spent some time in prison and was offered an opportunity to finish out his sentence in a mandated community residential treatment facility. For a couple of months, he completed program expectations with seeming ease. One night, after he had grown frustrated watching TV with some other residents, he walked out of the facility—this was viewed as abandoning treatment and would constitute a violation of his terms. His parole officer would have been authorized to take him back into custody and his sentence could have been extended another two years.

The treatment practitioner asked to talk with Carl and the parole officer, to see if there was another option that would allow Carl to come back to the residential program. The practitioner sought to understand Carl's perspective and believed that Carl had the best knowledge about himself and his needs. The practitioner wondered about whether there was a better way to support Carl's success if he returned to the program, what made him walk out, and what the practitioner could have done to help Carl in that moment.

Carl explained that people were making fun of him because the TV remote control was very complicated, and he could not figure out how to operate it. He thought that if he felt so "left behind" by technology, how could he make it in the world when he was released? The "plan" he developed in prison to be successful in the program addressed a variety of specific obstacles...but only the ones he could anticipate. His frustration about the remote control and fear of being out of step with new technologies was not something he had anticipated. He told the practitioner and his parole officer that what would help him would be to develop a plan of values and capacities that he could use for any situation he encountered, ones he anticipated and ones that he could not predict.

Being able to help a person succeed where they are *and* where they might be in the future is a way to strengthen long-term recovery.

TOOLS TO ENHANCE FOLLOWING THROUGH AND SUSTAINING CHANGE

Although change can be difficult, perhaps even more challenging is *sustaining* a change. In subsequent conversations, after a change plan is developed, we want to explore how the plan is going, affirm efforts the person is already making, and strengthen intentions to make a change in areas where the person is struggling. Bumps in the road *will* occur! People are likely to see these bumps as a failure and this can lead to a full recurrence of the pre-change situation or behavior. Practitioners can normalize this experience as a learning opportunity and use reflections, affirmations, and evocative questions to increase confidence and shift the focus from shame ("something must be wrong with me") to even more effective plans for continued growth.

Exploring values and goals can also increase motivation for follow-through. We can use a structured tool (e.g., values card sort) or simply explore what it would be like to live by certain important values and achieve certain goals. Values-based activity and goal identification increase the likelihood of follow-through and success.

Following Through

Here are some ideas about following through we can explore with people who already have good ideas for the next steps toward their change goal.

Do It First Thing in the Morning (or Close to It)

If we take even one small step that furthers our change before we do much of anything else, then we are more likely to honor that change, remember it, and make it a regular part of our lives. When we do it first thing in the morning (or close to it), it also becomes an item we can cross off the checklist for the day.

Find the Joy in It

It is sometimes the case that there is something absolutely delightful, rewarding, or joyful about our new decision. We may also choose to build a reward into our next steps to help us sustain our forward momentum. When we remember to savor this joy, it can help us keep the change motion.

"I'm going to _____ because I said so..."

Another small action that we can take to keep our change in motion involves printing out cards or jotting down notes that remind us of what we need to do to keep moving forward. We can write down, "I'm going to _____ because I said so," and fill in the blanks to the statement. This strategy helps us practice keeping our word to ourselves.

"My future self will thank me for doing _____ today."

Similar to the previous strategy, we can also print out notecards or jot down notes that say, "My future self will thank me for doing _____ today" and then fill in the sentiment. Doing so helps us think about what we can do right now to take good care of our future self, knowing that our future self will be grateful for what we're putting into motion right now.

Scaled Change

When we have a goal for ourselves, we can set a range around it to include the absolute minimum and absolute maximum we need to do to achieve that goal. For example, if we are already walking a total of two hours a week and our goal is to increase that to three hours a week, we might set the minimum to one hour a week and the maximum to four hours. Anything in that range, then, we can view as a success. It gives us some flexibility and lends an acceptance to our efforts—and it also reminds us that change can be on a continuum.

Schedule It

Another effective way to keep ourselves accountable is to schedule the change behavior on our calendar at a particular time, as if we have an appointment with ourselves. We can reinforce our completion of this activity with something that signifies success, happiness, achievement, or reward. For example, a smiley face or a sticker (for those of us who keep a paper calendar) or an emoji (for those of us who keep an electronic calendar).

The bubble sheet that follows is designed to be a way to structure a conversation about options for strengthening a person's follow-through with their change plans. A sample introduction might sound something like:

Practitioner: "Now that you've created your change plan, there are a variety of ways to support getting started and staying on track. If you are interested, I can tell you about these different methods. It's your choice whether you decide to use any of them."

Person: "Sure, anything that will help."

Practitioner: "On this bubble sheet I have a variety of strategies that people have found helpful for making a change and staying strong with it. Some are strategies that make it easier to start a change, like 'Do It (Almost) First Thing' and 'Schedule It.' They both have to do with the timing of the change during the day. Others involve reminders to keep going and stay strong with the change like 'My Future Self' and 'Because I Said So,' and others have to do with how the change is implemented, like 'Find the Joy,' which helps to associate the change with positive feelings, and 'Scaled Change,' which helps to set a minimum and maximum range for achieving a goal. For example, [an example that is relevant to the person's goals]. What do you think? What strategies, if any, would you like to explore further to support your change? You may have your own ideas about strategies to help you follow through with your plan. We have plenty of space here to add them!"

FOLLOWING-THROUGH AGENDA MAPPING

· · · · · ·

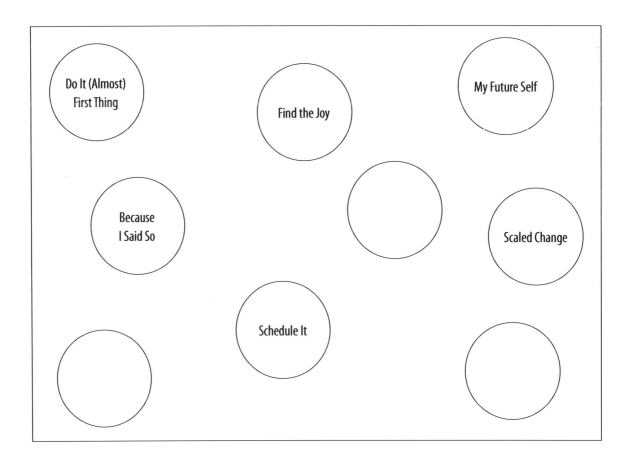

Between-Session Activities

Another way to support follow-through is to review between-session assignments at the beginning of each session. We can start by exploring the person's successes and partial successes to understand what is already working (e.g., time of day, method of record keeping, etc.) and then work on ideas for overcoming any barriers to completing between-session tasks:

- "Great, so you monitored your thoughts for three of the last seven days. What helped you to do that? What did you learn?"
- "I also noticed that it was easier for you to record your thoughts at night. What made that work for you?"
- "What about other times when it was harder for you to record your thoughts, what helped you do it anyway?"

If-Then Planning

If-then planning is a helpful way to remember plans for navigating barriers to follow through. If-then planning evokes the person's ideas for coping responses to situations that put them at risk for a recurrence or abandoning change efforts. The barriers the person identified on the Change Plan Worksheet may be included in the if-then plan, particularly if the person hasn't yet found ways to address them. As the person's if-then plans succeed, their confidence and ability to manage future difficulties increases, and they feel more motivated to continue to follow through with their plan.

If-then planning can also help a person get back on track following a recurrence of the behavior. Consider Jamal. He was doing well in treatment for co-occurring thought disorder and alcohol use disorder, then stopped taking his medications, relapsed to alcohol use, experienced severe symptoms of thought disorder, and ended up on a locked ward in the hospital.

Practitioner: "Sounds like you've had a tough few days."

Jamal: "I hate being locked in. They lock every door. I can't go anywhere."

Practitioner: "It's really hard for you being on this ward."

Jamal: "Yeah, it's rough. They were trying to get me in to that program but now I'm here. I hate it."

Practitioner: "I'm hearing that you'd like to avoid being back here in the future."

Jamal: "That would be good. Wouldn't be so bad if I could come and go."

Practitioner: "So you might be interested in going somewhere for treatment if you have some freedom while you're there."

Jamal: "Yeah, that would be okay, if I can go outside. I get really scared when I'm cooped up inside. The voices and shadows are really bad."

Practitioner: "You're saying that being cooped up makes the voices and the shadows worse. I also heard that some things were working well for you at the beginning of the week."

Jamal: "Yeah. I was doing good getting my medication."

Practitioner: "What helped you do that?"

Jamal: "We made a deal, you, me, and the doc. I tried to live up to it."

Practitioner: "So the deal worked, at least at first."

Jamal: "Yeah, I was doing pretty good. Then my wife was nagging me. I went out and got drunk."

Practitioner: "You were doing well before that."

Jamal [small smile]: "Yeah, I guess so."

Practitioner: "You tried to stick to our deal even though it was hard."

Jamal [nods]

Practitioner: "So you were doing your best to get to treatment when you got mad and drank, and that lead to you ending up here on the locked ward."

Jamal: "Yeah, I really don't like this."

Practitioner: "Well, what do you want to do now?"

Jamal: "I'll still go to treatment if they don't lock me up."

Practitioner: "So even with everything that has happened, you're still willing to try that program."

Jamal: "Yeah, I got to do something. But I'm worried about the rules and stuff."

Practitioner: "Sounds like you're worried about feeling nagged or losing your freedom. What helps when you feel stressed?"

Jamal: "I used to play all kinds of instruments."

Practitioner: "So it would be easier for you to tolerate if you can go outside sometimes and play music. What else?"

Jamal: "You know, if they nag me, I'm going to get really mad."

Practitioner: "So having a way to respond if you feel yourself getting mad, what would help there?"

Jamal: "Well, I used to draw. I'm pretty good. Maybe I could draw?"

Practitioner: "Sure, a lot of people find that a really good way to relax. Who might help you when you feel stressed to remember to go outside and walk or play music or draw? Who might you include in your plan?"

Jamal: "Could I call you?"

Practitioner: "Well, I think we could work something out with ways you could let me know you want to talk to me. Tim, too, if you want. What else?"

Jamal: "Would you tell them not to nag me?"

Practitioner: "Sure, we can talk to them about it together, how does that sound?"

Jamal: "Okay. That sounds good."

Practitioner: "What else would help you cope with stress?"

Jamal: "I'd like to see my wife, but if she starts nagging me, I'll go out and drink again!"

Practitioner: "Okay, so you might like it if we talk with your wife about things she could do instead of nagging. Is that right?"

Jamal: "Yup!"

Practitioner: "Okay, I think we can do that. And if you want to, there are family days at the program that might help with that, too. If you think you'd be interested."

Jamal: "I'll think about it."

Practitioner: "Okay. So, let me see if I understand what the plan is to help you stay here and at that treatment program when you get there…"

The practitioner summarizes their conversation and helps Jamal develop his if-then plan. His plan might look something like this:

Barriers	If this happens, then...	People who can help
My wife nags me sometimes, and program staff, too.	• I'll talk with her about other things she can do instead of nagging. • I could also try the family program at the treatment center.	• My social worker, Helen, will help me talk to my wife and the treatment program. • Tim, my peer worker—he gets it and makes me laugh.
My voices and shadows are worse when I feel stressed.	• I can take a walk outside. • I can draw. • I can play music.	• Jackie, the nurse, will sometimes take me outside for a walk. • Joe will bring me stuff for drawing. • I will try the music therapy.

As another example, Leona's if-then plan could look like this:

Barriers	If this happens, then...	People who can help
When I feel depressed, I don't follow my plan.	• I'll talk with Sheila about how I'm feeling. • I'll listen to my favorite song. • I'll contact Anna B. if my mood is low two days in a row.	• Sheila, my friend, will talk with me on the phone. • Anna B., my counselor, will schedule an extra session to address my low mood.
I can't stand the meditation classes right now.	• I can take the kids for a walk instead. • I can play video games or board games with the kids. • I can play music with the kids.	• My kids are fun to play with, and their silliness when we play games makes me laugh. • I will restart my music lessons.

IF-THEN PLANNING

• • • • • •

Name: _____ Date: _____

Barrier	If this happens, then...	People who can help

"Why, Can, and How" Cards to Sustain Change

When we reinforce reasons for change (why), our ability to change (can), and the steps we can take or have already taken toward change (how), we give it roots and nourish its growth. Once a person has a change plan in place, we can help them develop a simple tool to maintain momentum for change: a why, can, and how sheet or index card the person can take a few minutes each day to review. For example, a person's why, can, and how card might look like these:

Change Goal: Take my medications as prescribed.

Why: It will help me reduce anxiety.

Can: I am successful at things that are important to me.

How: I will put a note on the inside of the front door to remind me.

Change Goal: Get a job.

Why: I like to work, and the money will help me afford my rent and groceries.

Can: I enjoyed working before, and I am good at completing applications and interviews.

How: Every day I will spend 30 minutes looking at job listings and applying for jobs that I want. I will go to the interviews that are offered to me.

The DROP Worksheet

The DROP worksheet is a simple planning tool that incorporates elements of if-then planning along with the "why" and "how" of making a change. Change often feels gradual, much like adding drops of water to a bucket. Although it can be difficult when change does not happen immediately, adding daily drops to a "change bucket" increases a person's chances of success. These "DROPS" are formed by having the person:

- State a *desire* as it relates to a change goal: Why is your change goal important to you?
- Identify remaining internal *reluctance*: What are some things that get in the way of this goal?
- Specify a couple of *options* to get around that reluctance: What are some ways you can overcome these obstacles?
- Identify a possible *plan* that involves a small step (aka "drop") that moves the person toward their goal: What step are you going to take the next time that your reluctance tries to get in the way?

For example:

Change Goal: Take my medication as prescribed.

Desire: I want to feel better.

Reluctance: Sometimes when I'm out in public, I don't like others seeing me take medication.

Options: I could excuse myself and go get a glass of water. I could consider the timing of my medications and outings.

Plan: The next time I'm in public and it's time to take my medications, I'll try excusing myself to go get a glass of water.

THE DROP WORKSHEET

· · · · · ·

Name: _____ **Date:** _____

My Change Goal: _____

Desire (Why is your change goal important to you?):

_____

_____

_____

_____

Reluctance (What are some things that get in the way of this goal?):

_____

_____

_____

_____

Options (What are some ways you can overcome these obstacles?):

_____

_____

_____

_____

Plan (What steps can you take the next time that your reluctance tries to get in the way?):

_____

_____

_____

_____

THE DANCE OF MI: FROM PLANNING TO PREVENTING A RECURRENCE

As the person begins taking action on their plan, we guide toward increasing their commitment to making progress with their change. We support the person in reducing their risk of recurrence of the old behavior by:

- Helping them identify potential barriers to their progress.
- Exploring their good reasons and need for sustaining their commitment to the change long term.
- Working with them to modify their plan as needed to sustain their gains and continue their progress.

Signals to Increase Planning

- The person is expressing increased ambivalence for continuing the change.
- The person is struggling to adhere to their plan.
- The person may have initial success with the plan and then go back to the behavior they changed.

Practitioner Strategies to Increase Planning

- Convey acceptance and partnering to understand the person's perspective and dilemma.
- Normalize reluctance to continue the planning process due to the loss of other potential pathways to change (i.e., the path not taken).
- Explore the person's goals and how they are related to the change focus.
- Explore how the person would like to see themselves in the near and distant future related to the change focus.
- Follow the person's preference for addressing their underlying dilemma and resolving their ambivalence about the change focus:
    – Continue to work with the current change focus, evoking importance, confidence, and specific, concrete steps to make a revised plan for the current change focus, or
    – Refocus to a new change focus to address an underlying dilemma.
- Explore and affirm the person's values, strengths, and intentions related to the current or new change focus.

Signals to Guide Toward Recurrence Prevention

The person is keeping up with their plan for change and experiencing temptation to return to the old behavior or reduced interest in sustaining the change underway.

Practitioner Strategies to Guide Toward Recurrence Prevention

- Explore the benefits of the change so far and how their values are supported by the change.
- Explore temptation to return to old behavior and identify ways to address temptations.
- Partner to identify steps to solidify support for sustaining the change and help the person identify new change opportunities.
- Affirm the person's efforts, intentions, strengths, and skills for self-management of the change.
- Avoid taking over their change process and telling them what to do.
- Explore other changes they want to make.

CHAPTER SUMMARY

· · · · · ·

What do you see as the most important points of this chapter?

_____

_____

_____

_____

What interested you the most?

_____

_____

_____

_____

What planning strategies/tools do you think you most want to integrate into your work?

_____

_____

_____

_____

9

CONVERSATIONS ABOUT SUICIDE AND THE MI FOUR PROCESSES

I think one of our great tasks as human beings is to find the part of us that is big enough for life,
that can put its arms around the part that finds things difficult, that wants life to be different.

—David Whyte

IN THIS CHAPTER

- MI with People Experiencing Suicidal Thoughts and Intentions
- The Four Processes: Engaging
- The Four Processes: Focusing
- The Four Processes: Evoking
- The Four Processes: Planning
- Following Up

MI WITH PEOPLE EXPERIENCING SUICIDAL THOUGHTS AND INTENTIONS

A person's thoughts and intentions about suicide can be conceptualized as an internal conflict between the wish to live and the wish to die. Some evidence suggests that when a person's wish to live is as strong as or stronger than their wish to die, they are less likely to make a suicide attempt, and if they do, the attempt is less severe (Brown, Steer, et al., 2005; Kovacs & Beck, 1977). Increasing a person's motivation to live may reduce their risk of suicide and increase their engagement in mental health services (Britton et al., 2008; Britton, Patrick, Wenzel, & Williams, 2011).

MI is being explored as a brief intervention to reduce suicidality and increase safety over several sessions and as a single conversation designed to increase engagement in follow-up services (e.g., coping skills training, problem solving, substance use treatment; Britton, 2015). MI can be used during suicide risk assessment to evoke even more accurate information and increase intrinsic motivation to live (e.g., explore life-affirming reasons, activities, values, and beliefs).

In this chapter, we explore using MI to guide conversations about suicide risk and reasons to live using the four processes. In *engaging* we establish rapport, support autonomy, and avoid intensifying the person's natural conflict about talking about their suicidal thoughts. In *focusing* we identify the dilemmas underlying the person's thoughts of suicide. In *evoking* we strengthen the person's exploration of their reasons to live, stay safe, and make life worthwhile again. In *planning* we create plans that support the person's motivation to live. We collaborate with the person to remove suicide means and strengthen their ability to cope with periodic recurrences of suicidal thoughts and intentions.

Even our best MI efforts do not guarantee that we will be able to avoid involuntary commitment for safety reasons. However, embodying MI spirit in such conversations—like with any scenario that involves mandatory reporting—can increase the likelihood of repairing a rupture to the working alliance. Also, consultation with our fellow team members can provide excellent support as we navigate the challenge and complexities of these conversations.

THE FOUR PROCESSES: ENGAGING

> While supporting autonomy, it is important not to convey a message about a person's "right to suicide," as this may be perceived as condoning this action.

MI spirit increases engagement, suicide risk assessment accuracy, and opportunities to explore intrinsic reasons to live. We incorporate autonomy support where we can and balance that with transparency about the limits of confidentiality (Britton, 2015). This approach can be a shift for practitioners and organizations that routinely expedite hospitalization, whether or not the person agrees that it is necessary to maintain their safety. This can create a conflict for people who are thinking about talking with a practitioner about their suicidal thoughts but do not want to be forced into the hospital. Engaging begins with developing rapport by explaining our role, asking how the person prefers to be addressed, meeting in a comfortable and private setting, offering the person something to drink, and maintaining a calm, reassuring tone. As we explain the limits of confidentiality, we look for opportunities to clarify how we will support the person's autonomy. For example:

Practitioner: "Our conversations are in most cases confidential. That means that I will need your signed authorization before I can disclose information about our work together to people outside of this treatment setting. There are a few exceptions to this requirement that I'd like us to review together. I'm interested in your thoughts about this. There may be times when I may believe that there is a danger of harm to you or to another person. In those circumstances, I'm legally required to report this concern in order to ensure your safety and others' safety. What are your thoughts about that?"

Person: "Does that mean that you are going to hospitalize me if I talk about hurting myself?"

Practitioner: "That's a common concern, and I'm glad you raised it. My preference when I'm working with someone who is thinking about hurting themselves is to work together on identifying reasons to live and ways the person can keep themselves safe. In my experience, when people develop plans to make life worth living, there is no need for hospitalization. In the relatively infrequent event that hospitalization is necessary, I work with the person to identify ways to deal with the hospitalization, keep it as brief as possible, and create a plan for follow-up services that support the person's efforts to maintain their own safety. Given your concerns, how does this sound to you?"

Person: "Well, I guess it sounds okay. But really, I'm not saying I do, but if I wanted to kill myself you couldn't stop me. I could always find a way."

Practitioner [shifting focus to avoid argument]: "What you are saying is absolutely true and at the same time it sounds like you are willing to see how our work together might support your efforts to achieve some meaningful goals. Tell me about that. What are you hoping we'll accomplish here?"

It is not a simple task to maintain our empathy and appreciation of a person's strengths, skills, and resources when working with someone who is considering suicide. Empathizing with strong ambivalence about living is harder and takes longer than empathizing with strong ambivalence about other change goals. We are often pulled toward a deficit mindset, the belief that the person's insight, judgment, and emotional stability are not adequate to support their safety and well-being.

A deficit mindset increases the tendency to jump to conclusions, focus only on obtaining necessary information, obtain assurances of safety, and expedite hospitalization. Hospitalization alone is not a guarantee of effective treatment for reducing suicide risk (Chung et al., 2017, 2019). Conversations that prioritize obtaining assurances of safety over empathy and collaboration can increase suicide risk by intensifying discord and increasing service disengagement (Britton, 2015; Filiberti et al., 2001; Hendin, Haas, Maltsberger, Koestner, & Szanto, 2006; Zerler, 2007).

MI can make it easier to develop and maintain a working alliance while holding a focus on reducing risk, increasing safety, and increasing life-affirming behaviors. We ask necessary questions (e.g., "Are you feeling suicidal?") and explore important beliefs and experiences (e.g., "You feel hurt by your brother's attitude. How is that related to your current thoughts about harming yourself?") while demonstrating empathy and collaboration.

Respect, accurate empathy, autonomy support, and interest in the person's well-being open the door to greater self-acceptance and hope. What is often the most helpful in engaging a person who wishes to die into a conversation about commitment to life is the practitioner's ability to demonstrate deep understanding of the person's emotional experience:

"You are at the end of your tether." "This is unbearable for you."

This is counterintuitive. Practitioners most want to do everything possible to keep the person safe. Acting on the impulse to persuade the person to commit to life, however, can leave the person feeling invalidated, disrespected, and angry and ultimately increase the person's risk of attempting suicide. Accepting and resonating with the person's experience increases the person's sense of trust and openness to at least exploring other options and evoking motivation to live.

Thoughtful use of breaks and attending to personal needs and comfort increase the person's capacity for maintaining a calm, steady state for problem solving (Zerler, 2007).

In addition to the risk assessment, we want to understand the person's decision to talk with us from the perspective of why they chose *not* to make an attempt and what has helped them continue to choose to live. In addition to exploring strengths and resources, we may also explore beliefs and values that support the person's decision to stay safe. For example, a person might say something like, "I just don't see a point in struggling with this anymore." An MI practitioner could respond in a number of ways:

- **Guiding toward strengths:** "It's been a really long haul for you, and you feel like you are running out of steam for this. What has kept you going up to now?"

- **Guiding toward reasons for living:** "One part of you is exhausted by this struggle and another part of you brought you here to talk to me. Tell me more about the part inside you that wants to find a way to make life worth living."

- **Consolidating strengths and resources for envisioning goals:** "You've shown a lot of resilience making it this far with this burden on your own. And it takes a lot of courage to reach out for some assistance. What do you know about yourself that might help you be successful at making life worthwhile again?"

People sometimes enter conversations about suicide with reactance, apathy, helplessness, and/or an agenda that is not related to maintaining their own safety. In these circumstances, it is helpful to focus first on the person's strengths and resources to develop some safety and trust. Here are three examples of different situations and possible practitioner responses.

Situation 1: A person reports thoughts of suicide.

Practitioner response: "This is a hard thing to talk about and you've found the courage to reach out instead of making an attempt. Tell me about that; what prompted you to reach out?"

Situation 2: The person opts to go to the emergency room (ER), after a suicide attempt.

Practitioner response: "I understand that you found a way to get to the ER after making an attempt to commit suicide. That's not an easy thing to do. Tell me about what made you decide to reverse your action. What prompted you to reach out for assistance?"

Situation 3: Following an attempt, a person has been involuntarily admitted for evaluation and treatment.

Practitioner response: "It sounds like you were determined to die. Something must be very painful to make that decision. Tell me about how you managed to live with the pain for so long before you made this attempt."

Suicidality can also come up in an outpatient session as a person talks about past or present issues linked with suicidal behaviors (e.g., depression, anxiety, psychosis, substance use, trauma, medical issues). Sometimes we simply *think* they may be considering suicide. Whenever we think suicide might be an issue, we raise it using direct questions and follow up with empathic listening skills and compassion. Tara has already been working with the practitioner for a while:

Tara: "I've been having a lot more pain lately, and it has been making me really down."

Practitioner: "Tell me about that, what seems to be happening there?"

Tara: "Well, I was going to church and working part time and seeing my friends. But when the pain gets bad, I just stay home and watch TV. I've been feeling more depressed, and I don't want to talk to people because I don't want to worry them. I had to quit my job."

Practitioner: "In addition to the pain, it sounds like you've been feeling pretty down and isolated from your friends, and I know that job was important to you."

Tara: "Yes, that's true, I feel pretty depressed, and when my friends and my old boss call me, I just don't call them back."

Practitioner: "This sounds like a time you told me about before when you felt pretty bad and started seriously thinking about hurting yourself. Have those thoughts come back?"

Sometimes a person will respond to the direct question and sometimes they will avoid it. We continue trying to understand the person's current experience and, as appropriate, we move into focusing and ask permission to explore their consideration of suicide further.

THE FOUR PROCESSES: FOCUSING

The overall goal is to collaborate with the person on ensuring their safety until their risk of suicidality is consistently assessed as low, which may take a number of sessions. In focusing, we guide conversations in the direction of increasing safety, motivation to live, and reasons for living. We address critical underlying issues to increase the person's interest and ability for building a life worth living. Evidence suggests that suicide risk may decrease with assessment and interventions targeting (Brodsky, Spruch-Feiner, & Stanley, 2018; Jobes, 2017; Miller, Gaudiano, & Weinstock, 2016):

- Suicide risk factor identification.
- Values and goals clarification.
- Safety and future planning.
- Treatment engagement and follow-through.
- Improved person-support network problem solving.

Integrating MI into suicide risk assessment procedures and interventions may:

- Strengthen rapport, quality of information for effective safety planning, and interest in exploring ways to stay safe.
- Highlight and strengthen the person's own capacity to make decisions that help to maintain safety and reduce risk.
- Evoke the person's own positive expectations for and ability to engage effectively in follow-up services and activities.

Common focuses include risk factors that may be identified during a risk assessment, like:

- Long-term mental health issues (e.g., depression, anxiety, psychosis, substance use).
- Significant stressors (e.g., relational, vocational, health, etc.).
- Readiness for next steps in follow-up services.
- Coping with difficulties encountered in follow-up services.
- Readiness to continue to live.

As we navigate from one focus to another, we maintain awareness that the person can be in different stages of readiness for different focuses. For example, a person can commit to a plan for follow-up services and still be ambivalent about continuing to live (Zerler, 2007). Because of our legal and ethical responsibilities, some focuses will be higher priority than others when creating a plan for the next steps.

If we are unsure whether a person is considering suicide, we can introduce suicide as a focus and support collaboration by asking permission to talk about it: "You've had a rough go of it over the past month or so and you've been feeling more isolated from your friends and more depressed. It sounds like there's a chance you may have some thoughts of hurting yourself. It can be a hard thing to talk about. I wonder if we could talk about that possibility?"

If we don't feel that asking permission is appropriate, we can introduce the focus as a concern we have and follow up with empathy, collaboration, and autonomy support. In the following example, *focusing* transitions into the beginning of a risk assessment.

Practitioner: "I appreciate the strength it takes to tell me about feeling depressed, the physical pain, being cut off from your friends, and quitting your job. As I'm listening to you, I'm wondering where those feelings might lead. In the past they were connected to thoughts of harming yourself. Are you having thoughts about hurting yourself?"

Tara: "Okay, I admit I've thought about it. I don't want to make a big deal of this."

Practitioner: "I wonder if you would tell me more about those thoughts?"

Tara: "I cleaned out the medicine cabinet last week, and I found some medication that my mom stockpiled when she got sick. I just held onto it after she died. I put the medication back instead of just getting rid of it. I haven't been taking it or anything."

Practitioner: "You found the medication recently and you haven't been taking it yourself. But you've noticed some thoughts about hurting yourself. It sounds like hurting yourself is connected to holding on to your mom's old medication."

Tara: "You know, well…I didn't think about it before I cleaned out the cabinet. But yeah, I guess there's a connection."

Practitioner: "I really appreciate your willingness to talk with me about this. Could I ask how often the thoughts occur?"

The risk assessment continues, evoking the information that guides focusing for the rest of the conversation.

Thoughtful assessment of suicide risk factors and behaviors can engage people into understanding their behavior and finding safer and healthier ways of meeting their needs. To do this, we balance understanding the person's reasons and behaviors without intensifying overwhelming thoughts, feelings, and the perception of suicide as a solution (Britton, 2015). For example, when a person reports a suicide attempt, we ask about:

- Timing: When the attempt occurred.
- Method: What was used.
- Triggering event or reason: What was going on at the time the attempt occurred (e.g., stressors, events, reasons)?
- Why the attempt was unsuccessful: What contributed to the person's survival and subsequent motivation to live?

THE FOUR PROCESSES: EVOKING

The evoking phase is tailored to the person's level of risk and their willingness to explore reasons for living. This is an opportunity to decrease anxiety and conflict and increase the person's exploration of reasons for living, values, beliefs, and goals. As the person explores their reasons for living, the reasons become more meaningful and they develop interest in next steps that maintain their safety and increase their quality of life. We can support autonomy following the risk assessment by asking permission to continue to talk. For example:

Practitioner: "Tara, given what we've already talked about, I'm wondering if you would be willing to talk with me about what might happen next? I'm interested in your thoughts about what would be helpful in maintaining your safety and making life worthwhile."

Practitioner [Transitioning from risk assessment and a brief break, the practitioner summarizes Tara's risk factors and affirms her strengths]: "You've been dealing with a lot, the physical pain, feeling depressed and cut off from your family and friends, leaving your job, not wanting to reach out because you are worried about being a burden. That's a lot of stress at one time and a lot to deal with alone. It's been so painful that you've started thinking about how you might 'get it over with.' And there's your recent discovery of your mom's pills. I have to say that hearing all of this, I'm really impressed that you've been willing to talk to me about this today. That must have taken a lot of determination. There's a strong part of you that wants to get back to a life that feels manageable and worthwhile. Given everything we've been talking about, what do you feel you want most from our work together?"

Tara: "Well, this is the first time I've looked at it all together like this. I guess it has been building."

Practitioner: "You're surprised to hear everything you've been dealing with and that's helping you think about how you got to this place.'"

Tara: "I guess it makes sense to see it as feeling overwhelmed. Maybe it isn't realistic to think I can just snap out of it. It took time to get this way. Maybe we could talk about how to make it better?"

Practitioner: "You are willing to work together to find some strategies for dealing with your current stresses and create a more satisfying life."

Tara: "Maybe, what would that look like?"

Providing a Rationale for Interventions

As with other interventions, it is helpful to offer a tailored *rationale* for a risk-reducing intervention. Given the information evoked during engaging, focusing, and evoking, we shape the rationale for the proposed intervention to make it easy for the person to see how the approach can be helpful in their situation. For example:

Practitioner: "We do work with people who are feeling a lot of pain, like you are, the physical pain and the emotional pain. We're often able to work together with people on ways they can reduce their pain and live a more satisfying life. There is a priority I want to address today: reducing your risk of taking your mom's pills. In addition to that, we can talk about what would make life feel more meaningful and worthwhile. What do you think about all this?"

Strategically Evoking "Life Talk" and Exploring and Increasing the Motivation to Live

The evoking phase includes increasing change talk for engaging in services:

Tara: "I guess I can give that a try, you're saying there's a reason to believe things could change?"

Practitioner: "That's what other people have told us—that they found it helpful and hopeful. It sounds like you're thinking about it. If you decide to participate in these services, why would you do that?"

Tara: "Well, I guess I'm thinking about my friends and my church. If something happens to me, they might feel guilty? Like they didn't do enough? I guess that feels pretty important not to let that happen. They've tried pretty hard to reach out, and I've done my best to discourage them. It's not their fault."

> **Practitioner:** "So one thing you miss and want to get back to somehow is your time with your friends and your church. You are realizing that it's important to them and you."

> **Tara:** "Uh-huh, I guess. I didn't think about that before. I was just worried about being a burden to them." [evocation continues…]

Exploring the person's "life talk" while softening "suicide talk" (as with sustain talk) may help to reduce the risk and increase the likelihood of change in the direction of making life worth living.

Life Talk	Suicide Talk
• I want to make my life feel more worthwhile.	• I'm thinking about suicide almost all day.
• I can find a way to make my life more meaningful.	• I'm too agitated to do anything different.
• I need to take care of myself so I can take care of my cats.	• I don't deserve to live.
• I need to live.	• It doesn't matter what happens to me.
• I've decided that I am going to call my sister when I feel like a burden. She always helps me feel better.	• I'm better off alone, I just drag people down.
• I've started setting a reminder to go to bed earlier so I get more sleep.	• It's not worth it to try. Nothing I do makes it better.
• I'm already going to my community meetings every week to get out of the house.	• I just don't see any options for making life worthwhile. I don't fit in anywhere.

There are times when people are not ready to talk about reasons for living. In these circumstances, Britton (2015) recommends exploring the person's:

- Values and beliefs.
- Abilities.
- Strengths and accomplishments.
- Past experiences when things were going well and the person felt life was worth living.

This exploration can evoke the person's reasons and strengths for living. We may also use specific types of *reflections* to open up opportunities to shift suicide talk into life talk. For example:

> **Tara:** "I'm thinking about suicide almost all day."

> **Practitioner** [reframe]: "You see how those thoughts get in the way of appreciating the best things in your life."

> **Practitioner** [double-sided]: "One part of you is focused on suicide and there's another part of you that wants to show up for the important people in your life."

> **Practitioner** [agreement with a twist]: "You are noticing how often thoughts of suicide come up and you are looking for ways to focus more on the things that are most meaningful in your life."

REINFORCING CHANGE (LIFE) TALK, SOFTENING SUSTAIN (SUICIDE) TALK

· · · · · ·

Practitioner: "Tell me more about your relationship with your friends and your church. Why are they important to you?"

Tara: "When I feel up to it, I help out by singing with the choir and on some of the committees. The singing seems to relax me. I don't notice my pain as much then."

How might you respond to reinforce Tara's change talk?

_____

_____

_____

_____

_____

What MI skills did you use in your answer (i.e., open questions, affirmations, type of reflection, summarizing)?

_____

_____

_____

_____

Practitioner: "So when you volunteer at the church and sing, it lifts your spirits. You feel better physically, too."

Tara: "I guess that's true. And my friends are nice. They ask about me and tell stories that make me laugh. They are easy to be around."

How might you respond to reinforce her change talk?

_____

_____

_____

_____

_____

What MI skills did you use in your answer (i.e., open questions, affirmations, type of reflection, summarizing)?

_____

_____

_____

_____

_____

Practitioner: "They really care about you and like spending time with you."

Tara: "I guess so. But lately I feel like I'm dragging everyone down. Not that they've said anything about it."

How might you respond to soften her sustain talk and reinforce her change talk?

_____

_____

_____

_____

_____

What MI skills did you use in your answer (i.e., open questions, affirmations, type of reflection, summarizing)?

_____

_____

_____

_____

_____

Practitioner: "There are times when it's hard for you to join in, but they still reach out to see how you are doing."

Tara: "Well, that's true. Maybe I just worry about dragging them down."

How might you summarize her most important sustain talk and all of her change talk?

_____

_____

_____

_____

_____

Practitioner: "One part of you worries about being a burden and managing your pain, and another part of you sees how people enjoy spending time with you. It also sounds like that time with them and singing helps you feel better physically, too."

Tara: "Well, I guess that's true, I could do more to manage my pain better. I think that's a big reason I'm feeling so fed up with everything."

How might you express interest in her ideas for managing her pain?

_____

_____

_____

_____

_____

What MI skills did you use in your answer (i.e., open questions, affirmations, type of reflection, summarizing)?

_____

_____

_____

_____

_____

Note: Further exploration evokes her interest in feeling less depressed and boosting her income.

Practitioner: "So you've mentioned a number of things that could make life worthwhile: coming here, reconnecting with your friends and your church, working on feeling less depressed, enjoying your downtime more, finding ways to boost your income, and finding ways to better manage your physical pain. Thinking about all of this, where does it leave you?"

Tara: "I think I've been feeling pretty overwhelmed and I need to make some changes to make my life more manageable and worthwhile. I know I feel like it sometimes, but I really don't want to hurt myself."

How might you open the door to planning while supporting collaboration?

_____

_____

_____

_____

What MI skills did you use in your answer (i.e., open questions, affirmations, type of reflection, summarizing)?

_____

_____

_____

_____

Evoking Life Talk/Softening Suicide Talk

To reinforce a person's *life talk*, we reflect, affirm, and ask evocative questions to deepen the person's connection to making life more worthwhile. When we hear *suicide talk*, we respond in ways to soften it, and explore values, beliefs, strengths, accomplishments, and a time in their life when things were going well, and they felt their life was worth living. Skills we can use to soften suicide talk include simple reflections, reframing, double-sided reflection, agreement with a twist, evoking change talk, and shifting focus. For example:

> **Person:** "I still think of suicide all the time."

Possible practitioner responses:

> **Simple reflection:** "All of the time…"
>
> **Reframe:** "You are wondering how you might get started changing your focus to building a life that is important to you."
>
> **Double-sided reflection:** "One part of you is thinking about suicide, and another part of you is looking for better ways to manage your mood so you can look forward to your future again."
>
> **Agree with a twist:** "It's always there right now and you are looking to turn down the volume while you focus on what is most important to you to have in your life right now."
>
> **Shift focus:** "It feels that way now, and I get the sense there was a time when things were going well for you and life felt worth living. Tell me about how things were then?"

> **Person:** "I want to make my life feel more worthwhile."

Possible practitioner responses:

> **Reflect:** "You want your life to feel even more meaningful to you."
>
> **Affirm:** "Even though it's been tough on your own, you already have some ideas about how you can build the life you want for yourself."
>
> **Evoke:** "Tell me more about that. What would make your life more worthwhile? What is most important to you?"

EVOKING LIFE TALK/SOFTENING SUICIDE TALK

· · · · · ·

Respond to the following statements using each of the skills indicated. You can imagine what you "know" about the person to formulate your responses.

Person: "I'm too agitated to do anything different."

Reflect:

_____

_____

Reframe:

_____

_____

Double-sided reflection:

_____

_____

Agreement with a twist:

_____

_____

Shifting focus:

_____

_____

Person: "I need to take care of myself so I can take care of my cats."

Reflect:

_____

_____

Affirm:

_____

_____

Evoke:

_____

_____

Person: "I'm better off alone, I just drag people down."

Reflect:

_____

_____

Reframe:

_____

_____

Double-sided reflection:

_____

_____

Agreement with a twist:

_____

_____

Shifting focus:

_____

_____

Person: "I've decided that I am going to call my sister when I feel like a burden. She always makes me feel better."

Reflect:

_____

_____

Affirm:

_____

_____

Evoke:

_____

_____

Person: "It's not worth it to try. Nothing I do makes it better."

Reflect:

_____

_____

Reframe:

_____

_____

Double-sided reflection:

_____

_____

Agreement with a twist:

_____

_____

Shifting focus:

_____

_____

Person: "I've started setting a reminder to go to bed earlier so I get more sleep. It will help me feel better about everything."

Reflect:

_____

_____

Affirm:

_____

_____

Evoke:

_____

_____

Person: "I just don't see any options for making life worthwhile. I don't fit in anywhere."

Reflect:

_____

_____

Reframe:

_____

_____

Double-sided reflection:

_____

_____

Agreement with a twist:

_____

_____

Shifting focus:

_____

_____

Person: "I'm already going to my community meetings every week to get out of the house."

Reflect:

_____

_____

Affirm:

_____

_____

Evoke:

_____

_____

After exploring beliefs and values, strengths and accomplishments, and times when life was worthwhile, people may still struggle to identify a motivation to live. Reframing this perspective and asking about what would have to change to make life worthwhile may evoke some initial or implied life talk.

When the intention to commit suicide persists, people are in the midst of a suicidal crisis, and we may need to intervene with hospitalization and removal of means to commit suicide. We can still work with the person in a collaborative way by:

- Framing hospitalization as something that people often find helpful in reconnecting with a motivation for living;

- Exploring what might be difficult about hospitalization and how the person can cope with those challenges; and

- Envisioning with the person what their options are after discharge to maintain their safety and make their life feel even more worthwhile.

THE FOUR PROCESSES: PLANNING

During planning we work together with the person to consolidate their commitment to safety and living. For example:

> It is critical to have in place a safety plan that includes reducing access to means for suicide (e.g., weapons, medications).

> **Practitioner:** "Tara, it sounds like it might be a good time to talk about the next steps to make life more manageable and worthwhile, to help you stay safe, and to talk about what to do with your mom's pills. What do you think?"

The planning process can include increasing engagement in follow-up services, identifying barriers to engaging in services, and identifying ways to cope with barriers. Plans may also involve collaborative safety planning and collaborative crisis response planning to support the person's autonomy and address the person's current level of risk. For example, process steps may be created to help the person maintain their safety as they work toward developing their functional capacity to reduce their risk for recurrence of suicidal thoughts and intent.

Consolidating a Commitment to Life

Planning to consolidate motivation for and commitment to living follows from a person's readiness to commit to living. As with other mental health issues, this planning process can be initiated with open questions about next steps:

- "Tell me about where you want to start. What will make your life even more worthwhile?"

- "What might be your first steps for making life worth living?"

- "Where do you want to start?"

Planning continues with an exploration of a person's priorities for working toward an even more meaningful life:

> **Tara:** "Well, I want to see about improving my pain. I think I was better at it when I had a regular routine—my job, choir practice, Sunday school. I sort of organized things around being able to be on time for my commitments. I definitely see how I have some days that are worse than others, too.

> **Practitioner:** "So starting with pain management seems to be connected to some other priorities you've mentioned—work and returning to church. Something about a weekly schedule helps. And it sounds like a plan for when things feel dark might help, too."

> **Tara:** "That's true. I take better care of myself when I know others are counting on me to show up. I just don't feel up to it at all some days. I just go to bed and things get worse from there."

As the conversation continues, Tara explores how she might structure her weeks for better self-care. She comes up with some ideas about working from home that she hadn't considered before and a daily routine that will support her management of her physical pain and her mood. She is still experiencing more difficult periods when she feels more at risk for hurting herself and so the practitioner offers her the option of creating a crisis response plan.

Exploring Tara's motivation and good ideas for making life more meaningful and staying safe can include ways Tara might increase involvement with important people in her support network to help make her life more meaningful, help her deal with crises, and help remove access to means for suicide.

Collaborative Safety Planning

When there is access to means for suicide and a reason to believe that a person may be at risk, it is important to collaborate with the person to reduce the access to means. Collaborative safety planning involves working together with the person to identify their good ideas for staying safe and, as needed, personal resources and social supports to help with decreasing access or removing means for suicide. People are sometimes more ready to have this conversation after they've developed a plan to address issues that are important to them.

We transition to collaborative safety planning with a summary of the person's motivation and reasons to stay safe. We then evoke reasons for removing the means and invite the person's ideas about next steps for ensuring their safety.

COLLABORATIVE SAFETY PLANNING

• • • • • •

Practitioner: "You've worked hard to create a plan for addressing some of the issues that have felt overwhelming to you. Given how much pain you've been in and that your mom's pills are in your house, I'm wondering about your willingness to remove those to support your efforts to stay safe and feel better. What thoughts do you have about that?"

Tara: "If you suggested that when we started talking, I would have refused. Now that we've been talking about how bad I feel sometimes, I'm thinking that might actually be a good idea."

How would you respond to reinforce her change talk?

_____

_____

_____

_____

_____

What MI skills did you use in your answer (i.e., open questions, affirmations, type of reflection, summarizing)?

_____

_____

_____

_____

Practitioner: "So you are willing to think about it. You want to make sure you are safe. Why would you do that?"

Tara: "Well, I don't like the idea of how people would feel if something happened to me. And I've been thinking that when I start feeling better, I could do more for people who could use my help, like some of the people at my church."

How would you respond to reinforce her change talk?

_____

_____

_____

_____

_____

What MI skills did you use in your answer (i.e., open questions, affirmations, type of reflection, summarizing)?

_____

_____

_____

_____

_____

Practitioner: "You want to stick around for your friends and, given your skills, you are thinking you could help out others, too. Tell me more about that."

Tara: "Well, I've been thinking about talking with my pastor about how I might help with some of our fundraising. And maybe some older folks need a bit of help sorting out their finances. Not right now, but when I'm feeling better."

How would you respond to reinforce her change talk?

_____

_____

_____

_____

_____

What MI skills did you use in your answer (i.e., open questions, affirmations, type of reflection, summarizing)?

_____

_____

_____

_____

_____

Practitioner: "Those sound like very worthwhile projects. And you see how getting rid of the medication stash would be an investment in getting involved in those projects in the future."

Tara: "Yeah. It gets pretty bad some days, so I guess I should do it now."

How would you respond to evoke her good ideas?

_____

_____

_____

_____

What MI skills did you use in your answer (i.e., open questions, affirmations, type of reflection, summarizing)?

_____

_____

_____

_____

Practitioner: "What thoughts do you have about how you might do that?"

Tara: "Well, I could flush them right when I get home today, just take care of it while I'm thinking about it."

How would you respond to reinforce her commitment speech?

_____

_____

_____

_____

Practitioner: "That sounds like a commitment you want to make. That you will flush them when you get home."

Tara: "I will. I want to do it while I'm still focused on maintaining my safety. I never should have held onto those pills in the first place."

How would you summarize her plan for safety and ask permission to talk more about it in her next session?

_____

_____

_____

_____

_____

Practitioner: "You sound committed to removing the medications from your house by flushing them. You've worked really hard today putting together plans for making life more manageable and maintaining your safety. You've come up with a lot of good ideas. I wonder if it would be okay to talk with you about this again at our next session, to see how it's going for you."

Tara: "Okay, that would be good. It sounds pretty hard, but I do have some ideas to make it easier to deal with things. I might even call my pastor before I see you again to talk about my ideas."

How might you summarize and wrap up the session?

_____

_____

_____

_____

_____

Collaborative Crisis Response Planning

Moments of elevated suicide risk are often brief and fleeting (Simon et al., 2013), but sometimes a person's thoughts about suicide become overwhelming. *Crisis response planning* (Bryan et al., 2017) is a collaborative planning process designed to increase coping with periodic episodes of intense distress, to interrupt the experience before it becomes overwhelmingly unmanageable and activates thoughts of suicide as a solution. Working together with the person, we guide their exploration of each step as they handwrite their plan. Ultimately, the person either carries the plan with them or takes a picture of it to keep on their phone to serve as a reminder of what to do when they start to feel overwhelmed. The steps for making a crisis response plan involve identifying:

- Personal warning signs (i.e., a behavior, emotion, and thought) that indicate they are heading toward an intense emotional crisis.
- Simple strategies they will use to reduce stress or distract themselves from intense emotions.
- Reasons for living, the things that provide a sense of purpose or meaning in their life
- Friends and family members who will provide support or help lift their mood when they are struggling.
- Contact information for health care practitioners, crisis hotlines, and emergency services.

Figure 11 shows an example of a crisis plan for Tara.

Warning signs I will watch for:
- Avoiding friends (not answering phone).
- Feeling down, trapped.
- Thinking it will never get better.

Possible strategies I can use to feel better:
- Sing "Amazing Grace" and "Still I Rise"
- Pray
- Play with my cat
- Read inspirational poetry and favorite Bible passages
- Recall my favorite experiences with Sunday school and choir
- Watch favorite videos

My reasons for *living*:
- I have people in my life who care about me and who would be hurt if I were gone.
- I have some new options for managing my pain.
- I love the natural world.
- I have new ideas about how to make my work more rewarding.
- I love to sing!

People in my life who will support me:
- My sister Deb, [phone number]
- My friends Mary, [phone number], and Helen, [phone number]
- Pastor Anthony, [phone number]

Professional resources:
- My social worker, Dan Smith, [phone number]
- The hotline, 1-800-273-8255 (TALK)

Things I can do if my thoughts and feelings become overwhelming:
- Call 911
- Go to the hospital

Figure 11. Crisis Plan for Tara

People are not always ready to take steps and make a plan. Rather than forcing planning and increasing the person's defensiveness, it can be helpful to remember that most of the decision making in a change process occurs outside of the session. Our role is sometimes to help the person begin with process steps that help them maintain their safety and autonomy (i.e., committing to stay safe until the next session, committing to call the suicide prevention lifeline or go to the ER if their suicidal thoughts intensify or they feel unable to keep themselves safe). In future sessions, we can then ask permission to follow up with their thoughts on functional changes that increase commitment to life and reduce the likelihood of recurrence. Follow-up sessions are very helpful for collaborating on addressing unexpected barriers to safety plans and maintaining a motivation for change.

FOLLOWING UP

In follow-up sessions we continue to maintain the working alliance and focus on reducing suicide risk. Periodic use of screening instruments with predictive validity (see Appendix, "Suicide Risk Resources") are often used for ongoing risk assessment and for focusing treatment. Assessed risk levels offer a starting point for identification of ongoing issues underlying the person's current suicidal thoughts. We can initiate the conversation by identifying the focus issues in the context of the person's wise choices, strengths, and progress so far:

> **Practitioner:** "We've been working on your plan for reducing your risk for suicide and making your life feel even more worthwhile. You've disposed of your mom's medication stash and even called your pastor about your ideas for helping out at the church more. I'm looking at your responses to this assessment and wondering what you feel is contributing to your current thoughts about suicide?"

> **Tara:** "Well, it's actually better since I talked to my pastor, I'm less worried about going back to church when I'm ready. And I'm using my plan when I get really down. I'm still struggling with the pain; it makes me feel trapped and irritated sometimes. If we could work on managing the pain and irritation, I think that would help."

> **Practitioner:** "Yes, we can prioritize managing the pain and the irritation. If you're willing, I'm wondering how you managed to call your pastor. I know you had some concerns about that. Would it be okay if we explore that briefly together? I think it might help with our focus today."

> **Tara:** "Yeah, it's okay. I was pretty embarrassed when I called him because it's been a while. But he was really nice. He didn't pressure me to come back to church. He just told me he'd be happy to talk anytime about my ideas. He seems genuinely interested."

> **Practitioner:** "It sounds like you found a way to manage your embarrassment really well and followed through on your plan to keep yourself safe, and you talked to him. How are you doing all of that?"

> **Tara:** "I keep thinking about how my friends and the people at church would feel if I hurt myself and how I don't want them to feel bad. That helps. And my pastor said he appreciated my reaching out. It really wasn't easy. But it helps thinking about helping others."

> **Practitioner:** "So, focusing on how others will feel if something happens to you, having routines to support your goals, and having people who care about you without making demands on you all make taking care of yourself manageable even when it feels hard. How might these ideas help you with managing your pain and irritation? Or maybe you have other ideas?"

In follow-up sessions we continue our collaboration to identify key issues (e.g., depressed mood, substance use, etc.) that will directly reduce the person's risk for suicide and enhance safety and well-being. We evoke reasons for living and commitment to plans that help the person maintain their own safety. And we maintain our awareness that the person's readiness to live may be different from the person's readiness to commit to a plan that helps them maintain their own safety. We continue to work together to increase engagement in services and activities that support the person's efforts to sustain their own safety and enhance their life.

CHAPTER SUMMARY

• • • • • •

What do you see as the most important points of this chapter?

_____

_____

_____

_____

_____

What interested you the most?

_____

_____

_____

_____

_____

What information seemed most relevant to your practice?

_____

_____

_____

_____

_____

_____

10

NEXT STEPS: CONTINUING YOUR MI JOURNEY

You know what? When I left the Intro to MI training, I thought I was ready to use it.
Here I am six weeks into our work as a team and I'm just beginning to appreciate
how complex it is. I want to learn to do this well. What else do I need?

—Training Participant

IN THIS CHAPTER

- Coaching and Coding
- Communities of Practice
- Self-Assessment and Peer Feedback
- Tools and Exercises for Continued Growth

Developing MI competence and integrating it into routine practice requires more than an introductory MI training (Miller & Moyers, 2006; Miller & Rollnick, 2013; Miller et al., 2004; Moyers, Miller, & Hendrickson, 2005). Initial skillfulness erodes quickly, unless followed up with professional coaching, coding, ongoing self-assessment, peer feedback, and targeted practice (Miller & Moyers, 2006; Miller & Rollnick, 2013; Miller, Yahne, Moyers, Martinez, & Pirritano, 2004). In this chapter we look at ways to strengthen your MI skills and integrate them into your everyday practice using peer-based collaborative practice activities, feedback, and MI fidelity measures. Working within a *community of practice* provides structured support for these activities.

COACHING AND CODING

MI skill coaching provides feedback and skill development based on a practitioner's recorded or live practice sample (i.e., a conversation about change). Coaches evoke the practitioner's observations, offer feedback on strengths and *stretches* (next steps), and scaffold practice options to strengthen MI-consistent behaviors and reduce reliance on MI-inconsistent behaviors.

MI coaches use coding systems to provide more reliable and objective feedback on practice. MI coding systems measure fidelity to MI spirit and skills. Learning to use reliable MI coding systems helps practitioners increase their own MI proficiency and strengthens their ability to provide helpful feedback and coaching to their colleagues. MINT members offer training on several coding systems.

Motivational Interviewing Treatment Integrity (MITI): The most commonly used coding system (Moyers, Rowell, Manuel, Ernst, & Houck, 2016), the MITI offers reliable and objective feedback on practitioner behaviors (e.g., expression of empathy, cultivating change talk, softening sustain talk, partnering, MI-consistent behaviors, MI-inconsistent behaviors). (http://casaa.unm.edu/codinginst.html)

Motivational Interviewing Skills Code (MISC): The MISC (Houck et al., 2010) offers reliable and objective feedback on practitioner skill and is used for MI process research. The MISC looks at the relationship between the practitioner's behaviors and the behaviors of the person talking about making a change. The MISC is used to generate new knowledge about MI and its effectiveness. (http://casaa.unm.edu/codinginst.html)

Motivational Interviewing Competency Assessment (MICA): This is the newest coding system on this list. According to a paper posted on the MICA website, it offers promise as a feedback tool. MICA measures five MI intentions (partnering, guiding, supporting autonomy and activation, expressing empathy, and evoking) and two MI strategies (strategically responding to sustain talk and strategically responding to change talk). The intentions are derived from MI spirit or style (i.e., partnership, acceptance, compassion, evocation), along with principles of self-determination and health activation. The strategies apply to the technical use of MI skills. (www.micacoding.com). For more information on accessing the MICA, contact Ali Hall at https://motivationalinterviewing.org/profile/AliHall.

COMMUNITIES OF PRACTICE

A learning community or learning network is a real or virtual network of practitioners and/or trainers who all practice or who are interested in developing practice in the same arena, in this case, Motivational Interviewing. A community can be both a resource and a home for resources, and also a forum for the development of practice.

—MINT, 2019

Learning together is more rewarding and fun than learning alone. Talking about MI is unlikely to increase skillfulness. Regularly practicing together increases MI skillfulness, service outcomes, and work satisfaction. Communities of practice use *intentional feedback*, *practice*, *planning*, and *structure* to support ongoing MI skill development. MINT suggests:

- Get together regularly (in person or virtually) for meetings, trainings, seminars, workshops, and development days.
- Work together to identify shared goals and values and make plans for sustaining and improving MI practice.
- Identify individual and shared roles and responsibilities within the community of practice.
- Create and maintain opportunities for feedback from professional coaches and peers.

Meeting at least once every two weeks and using most of the meeting for practice strongly supports skill development. Listening to each other's actual practice recordings adds even more opportunities for rewarding experiences through thoughtful feedback, practice, and appreciation of strengths and skills.

> In-depth information on forming and working within communities of practice is available on the MINT website: *Creating a Motivational Interviewing Learning Community: Guidance from the Motivational Interviewing Network of Trainers* (2019).

SELF-ASSESSMENT AND PEER FEEDBACK

What you pay attention to grows.

—Deepak Chopra

Coding systems require substantial training and quality assurance to ensure coder reliability. However, even where we do not have access to a trained coder, we can self-assess or offer each other helpful feedback, based on what we observe from recordings of actual practice or live observations of conversations about change. We might:

- Listen for and count reflections and questions, with a goal of achieving a ratio of at least two reflections to every question.

- Listen for a person's change talk and count the skills used to elicit or respond (e.g., questions, reflections, affirmations, summaries), working to increase responses that elicit change talk.

- Listen for and count MI-consistent behaviors (e.g., affirmations, seeking collaboration, emphasizing autonomy) and MI-inconsistent behaviors (e.g., persuasion without permission, confrontation).

- Listen for how the practitioner navigates the four processes, and assess the quality of the relationship (i.e., practitioner partnering and empathy).

Another way to self-assess or provide feedback to a colleague is by rating conversations using coding systems to differentiate between MI-inconsistent and MI-consistent conversations. You can try this out for yourself or with a colleague. Using the Partnering for Change scale that follows (from the Abbreviated Motivational Interviewing Competency Assessment [A-MICA]), listen to a recording and try choosing the appropriate partnering code. What do you notice about how a scale like this might help you to identify skills you want to develop or strengthen? How might a scale like this make it easier to describe practitioner behaviors and consider next steps in skill development?

PARTNERING FOR CHANGE

• • • • • •

This scale measures the extent to which the practitioner fosters a collaborative process with a person as two *equal* partners who are working together toward the person's goals. There is a shared balance of power, and the person is the acknowledged expert regarding their life.

MI-INCONSISTENT RESPONSES (0)	BEGINNING TO SOUND PERSON-CENTERED RESPONSES (1)	MI-CONSISTENT RESPONSES (2)
The Practitioner: • Exerts the expert role by defining the person's problem and prescribing, developing, and/or planning for the person. • Gives advice or suggestions without permission. • Exhibits the righting reflex in a condescending and patronizing way. • Is indifferent to or unaware of interpersonal discord. • Makes minimal attempts to engage or build rapport.	**The Practitioner:** • Makes efforts to collaborate and share decision making. • Asks permission or secures an invitation before offering advice or suggestions. • Shows efforts to manage the righting reflex successfully. • Is aware of any discord or reactance if it arises and makes some attempt to reduce it and reengage. • Conveys the belief that the person can contribute meaningfully to the change process.	**The Practitioner:** • Skillfully collaborates with and empowers the person. • Acts as a key consultant, working with the person within their change process. • Augments the person's change process with relevant knowledge and expertise when requested or if permission is asked and given. • Successfully avoids the righting reflex. • Elicits/Evokes and reinforces the person's expertise, insights, and ideas relevant to their change process.

Structured self-assessment can help you avoid skills erosion over time and plan for further skills development. The Weekly Assessment and Action Plan can help you assess where you are and what you might want to change. You may want to make copies so that you can use it regularly.

WEEKLY ASSESSMENT AND ACTION PLAN

. . . . . .

What I learned this week from my motivational conversations:

_____

_____

_____

_____

_____

Skills I tried this week:

_____

_____

_____

_____

People or other resources that can support me in applying my insights and skills:

_____

_____

_____

_____

_____

DEEPENING UNDERSTANDING OF PARTNERING

• • • • • •

This creative exercise is particularly effective as a group exercise within your community of practice. It will also work as a partner exercise or as a solo exercise. It draws on the concept that, as we noted in Chapter 5, creative activities help people look at information from a fresh perspective, increasing insight and connections among concepts, flexibility, and new ideas (Birgilli, 2015; Chan, 2013).

What you will need:

· Multiple copies of this exercise and the Partnering for Change tool (if it will be a group exercise).

· Large sheets of paper.

· Markers, crayons, etc.

· Magazines, stickers, icons; any creative materials you'd like!

Process

As a group, listen to a recorded conversation about change.

Ask each member to describe the conversation using words, drawings, magazine cutouts, stickers, etc.

Consider these questions:

· What did the conversation feel and sound like? How would you describe its overall temperature?

· What were the practitioner's strengths?

· Was the conversation more a one-way street, with the practitioner telling, educating, fixing? Or more like a two-way street, where the practitioner and the person each had meaningful expertise?

· How would each of you rate the conversation on the Partnering for Change scale?

· What might have made the conversation even more MI consistent?

Share your visual descriptions with one another and consider:

· How do your descriptions resonate with or differ from one another?

· How has your understanding of the difference between unskillful and skillful MI practice deepened from this exercise?

MI-INCONSISTENT TO MI-CONSISTENT PARTNERING

• • • • • •

When you look at the list of *MI-inconsistent behaviors* (0 rating) on the Partnering for Change Scale, what images, words, feelings arise for you?

Images	Words	Feelings

When you look at the list of *MI-consistent* behaviors (2 rating), what images, words, feelings arise for you?

Images	Words	Feelings

As you think about your future conversations about change, what images, words, pictures, illustrations, descriptions, etc., will you hold in your heart and mind to help you aim toward MI-consistent behaviors?

_____

_____

_____

_____

_____

PARTNERING FOR CHANGE

· · · · · ·

Listen to a colleague's recorded conversation about change and:

- Identify your colleague's partnering strengths.

- Evoke from your colleague the skill they most want to strengthen.

- Practice that skill together.

- Notice how identifying your own and others' MI skills enriches your ideas for strengthening your own skills.

MY VALUES AND CHANGES I WANT TO SEE

· · · · · ·

This is a tool to help start a conversation about values and goals within an organization/community of practice.

Why do you do the work that you do?

_____

_____

_____

_____

What do you see as the role, purpose, or mission of your work?

_____

_____

_____

_____

What is your role on your team (include specific program if applicable)?

_____

_____

_____

_____

How do your top values relate to your work?

_____

_____

_____

_____

What are your *personal* goals for using MI to make your conversations about change even more effective?

_____

_____

_____

_____

What might need to shift in your *program's* culture and/or environment to support even more effective conversations about change?

_____

_____

_____

_____

How do your top values relate to the changes you would like to see in your program's culture or environment?

_____

_____

_____

_____

PLANNING FOR TEAM SKILLS DEVELOPMENT

• • • • • •

This implementation planning activity is designed to be completed in brief manageable chunks of time over many meetings. If you plan to do this activity in your community of practice meetings, remember to save most of your time in each meeting for practicing skills.

To begin this activity, discuss with your team the changes you envision for your program or organization. Identify one specific change in your program, organizational culture, or environment that will help you do an even better job supporting:

- Partnering (i.e., respect, understanding the other person's perspective and wisdom).
- Acceptance (i.e., autonomy, recognizing strengths and potential, empathy, absolute worth).
- Compassion (i.e., the interests of the people you serve and each other's growth).
- Evocation (i.e., supporting increased participation by the people you serve in expressing their own priorities, good ideas, and wisdom for change; and supporting your own and your team members' growth).

Use large sheets of paper to envision the pathway to your organizational goals. Remember to pace yourselves and reserve most of your meeting time for skills practice. You might plan to complete one sheet of paper for each of these areas:

- Your mission (organizational, specific program, or team).
- Values that drive the mission.
- Desired organizational outcomes (i.e., specifically what will change or improve as a result of your effort, such as "Physical space, processes, and/or procedures will be more engaging," "Conversations about change will be more MI consistent").
- Implementation plan (how changes will be implemented).
- Anticipated implementation challenges (what is sustaining the way things are done now?).
- Potential solutions/strategies.
- How you will measure your progress (i.e., engagement and retention rates, development of MI feedback and coaching, etc.).
- How you will sustain your successes/innovations.
- Create a timeline for next steps (e.g., who is doing what, when?).
- Resources or additional information you will need to be successful.

Note: See also the MINT's *Implementing Motivational Interviewing*: https://motivationalinterviewing.org/implementing-motivational-interviewing.

FINALLY...

We hope this toolkit is helpful to you as you practice applying MI in your conversations about change.

We hope you seek feedback and coaching from an experienced MI coach using a reliable and objective coding system.

We hope your efforts to develop MI proficiency increase your effectiveness and your satisfaction with your work.

We hope you practice MI with your colleagues and that it makes your services even more effective.

Most of all, we hope you experience greater compassion and understanding for yourself and for those with whom you work.

CHAPTER SUMMARY

• • • • • •

What do you see as the main points of this chapter?

_____

_____

_____

_____

What learning strategy or strategies from this chapter are you most likely to try within the next few weeks?

_____

_____

_____

_____

REFERENCES

For your convenience, the worksheets and forms from this book are available for download at www.pesi.com/FreyHall

Amrhein, P. C., Miller, W. R., Yahne, C. E., Palmer, M., & Fulcher, L. (2003). Client commitment language during motivational interviewing predicts drug use outcomes. *Journal of Consulting and Clinical Psychology, 71,* 862–878.

Arkowitz, H., Westra, H. A., Miller, W. R., & Rollnick, S. (Eds.). (2008). *Motivational interviewing in the treatment of psychological problems.* New York: Guilford Press.

Balán, I. C., Lejuez, C., Hoffer, M., & Blanco, C. (2016). Integrating motivational interviewing and brief behavioral activation therapy: Theoretical and practical considerations. *Cognitive and Behavioral Practice, 23*(2), 205–220.

Bandura, A. (1994). *Self-efficacy: The exercise of control.* New York, NY: Freeman.

Bem, D. (1972). Self-perception theory. In L. Berkowitz (Ed.), *Advances in experimental social psychology* (Vol. 6, pp. 2–62). New York, NY: Academic Press.

Bilderbeck, A. C., Saunders, K. E., Price, J., & Goodwin, G. M. (2014). Psychiatric assessment of mood instability: Qualitative study of patient experience. *British Journal of Psychiatry, 204*(3), 234–239.

Birgili, B. (2015). Creative and critical thinking skills in problem-based learning environments. *Journal of Gifted Education and Creativity, 2*(2), 71–80.

Bjornestad, J., Lavik, K. O., Davidson, L., Hjeltnes, A., Moltu, C., & Veseth, M. (2019). Antipsychotic treatment—a systematic literature review and meta-analysis of qualitative studies. *Journal of Mental Health, 12,* 1–11.

Bjornestad, J., Veseth, M., Davidson, L., Joa, I., Johannessen, J. O., Larsen, T. K., … Hegelstad, W. T. (2018). Psychotherapy in psychosis: Experiences of fully recovered service users. *Frontiers in Psychology, 9.* Retrieved from https://www.ncbi.nlm.nih.gov/pmc/articles/PMC6131645/

Bohart, A. C., Elliott, R., Greenberg, L. S., & Watson, J. C. (2002). Empathy. In J. C. Norcross (Ed.), *Psychotherapy relationships that work* (pp. 89–108). New York, NY: Oxford University Press.

Bordin, E. S. (1979). The generalizability of the psychoanalytic concept of the working alliance. *Psychotherapy: Theory, Research & Practice, 16*(3), 252–260.

Bradshaw W., Roseborough, D., & Armour, M.P. (2006). Recovery from severe mental illness: The lived experience of the initial phase of treatment. *International Journal of Psychosocial Rehabilitation, 10*(1), 123–131.

Brehm, S., & Brehm, W. (1981). *Psychological reactance: A theory of freedom and control.* New York, NY: Academic Press.

Britton, P. C. (2015). Motivational interviewing to address suicidal ideation. In H. Arkowitz, R. W. Miller, & S. Rollnick (Eds.), *Motivational interviewing in the treatment of psychological problems* (pp. 193–218). New York, NY: Guilford Press.

Britton, P. C., Patrick, H., Wenzel, A., & Williams, G. C. (2011). Integrating motivational interviewing and self-determination theory with cognitive behavioral therapy to prevent suicide. *Cognitive and Behavioral Practice, 18*(1), 16–27.

Britton P. C., Williams, G. C., & Conner, K. R. (2008). Self-determination theory, motivational interviewing, and the treatment of clients with acute suicidal ideation. *Journal of Clinical Psychology, 64*(1), 52–66.

Brodsky, B. S., Spruch-Feiner, A., & Stanley, B. (2018). The zero suicide model: Applying evidence-based suicide prevention practices to clinical care. *Frontiers in psychiatry, 9*(33).

Brown, G. K., Have, T. T, Henriques, G. R., Xie, S. X. Hollander, J. E., & Beck, A. T. (2005). Cognitive therapy for the prevention of suicide attempts: A randomized controlled trial. *Journal of the American Medical Association, 294*(5), 563–570.

Brown, G. K., Steer, R. A., Henriques, G. R., & Beck, A. T. (2005). The internal struggle between the wish to die and the wish to live: A risk factor for suicide. *American Journal of Psychiatry, 162,* 1977–1979.

Bryan, C. J., Mintz, J., Clemans, T. A., Leeson, B., Burch, T. S., Williams, S. R., … Rudd, M. D. (2017). Effect of crisis response planning vs. contracts for safety on suicide risk in U.S. Army Soldiers: A randomized clinical trial. *Journal of Affective Disorders, 212,* 64–72.

Carey, K. B., Leontieva, L., Dimmock, J., Maisto, S. A., & Batki, S. L. (2007). Adapting motivational interventions for comorbid schizophrenia and alcohol use disorders. *Clinical Psychology: Science and Practice, 14*(1), 39–57.

Chan, Z. C. (2013). Exploring creativity and critical thinking in traditional and innovative problem-based learning groups. *Journal of Clinical Nursing, 22*(15–16), 2298–2307.

Chung, D., Hadzi-Pavlovic, D., Wang, M., Swaraj, J, Olfson, M., & Large, M. (2019). Meta-analysis of suicide rates in the first week and the first month after psychiatric hospitalization. *BMJ Open, 9*(3). Retrieved from https://bmjopen.bmj.com/content/9/3/e023883

Chung, D. T., Ryan, C. J., Hadzi-Pavlovic, D., Singh, S. P., Stanton, C., & Large, M. M. (2017). Suicide rates after discharge from psychiatric facilities: A systematic review and meta-analysis. *Journal of the American Medical Association Psychiatry, 74*(7), 694–702.

Deci, E. (1980). *Self-determination.* Lexington, MA: Lexington Books.

Dobber, J., Latour, C., de Haan, L., Peters, R., Barkhof, E., & van Meijel, B. (2018). Medication adherence in patients with schizophrenia: A qualitative study of the patient process in motivational interviewing. *BMC Psychiatry, 18,* Article 135.

Dobber, J., Latour, C., van Meijel, B., Ter Riet, G., Barkhof, E., Peters, R., Scholte Op Reimer, W. & de Haan, L. (2020). Active ingredients and mechanisms of change in motivational interviewing for medication adherence: A mixed methods study of patient-therapist interaction in patients with schizophrenia. *Frontiers in Psychiatry, 11,* Article 78.

Emmons, R. A., & McCullough, M. E. (2003). Counting blessings versus burdens: Experimental studies of gratitude and subjective well-being in daily life. *Journal of Personality and Social Psychology, 84*(2), 377–389.

Emmons, R. A., & Mishra, A. (2012). Why gratitude enhances well-being: What we know, what we need to know. In K. Sheldon, T. Kashdan, & M. F. Steger (Eds.), *Designing the future of positive psychology: Taking stock and moving forward* (pp. 248–262). New York, NY: Oxford University Press.

Filiberti, A., Ripamonti, C., Totis, Al, Ventafidda, V., De Conno, F., Contiero, P., & Tamburini, M. (2001). Characteristics of terminal cancer patients who committed suicide during a home palliative care program. *Journal of Pain and Symptom Management, 22*(1), 544–553.

Gordon, T. (1970). *Parent effectiveness training.* New York, NY: Wyden.

Hanh, T. N. (2014). *The art of communicating.* New York, NY: HarperOne.

Hendin, H., Haas, A. P., Maltsberger, J. T., Koestner, B., & Szanto, K. (2006). Problems in psychotherapy with suicidal patients. *American Journal of Psychiatry, 163*(1), 67–72.

Hirschfeld, R. M., Lewis, L., & Vornik, L. A. (2003). Perceptions and impact of bipolar disorder: How far have we really come? Results of the national depressive and manic-depressive association 2000 survey of individuals with bipolar disorder. *Journal of Clinical Psychiatry, 64*(2), 161–174.

Hofmann, S. G., Grossman, P., & Hinton, D. E. (2011). Loving-kindness and compassion meditation: Potential for psychological interventions. *Clinical Psychology Review, 31*(7), 1126–1132.

Houck, J. M., Moyers, T. B., Miller, W. R., Glynn, L. H., & Hallgren, K. A. (2010). *Motivational Interviewing Skill Code (MISC) 2.5.* Retrieved from http://casaa.unm.edu/download/misc25.pdf

Ingersoll, K. S., Wagner, C. C., & Gharib, S., (2002). *Motivational groups for community substance abuse programs.* Richmond, VA: Mid-Atlantic Addiction Technology Transfer Center.

Jackson, C., Butterworth, S., Hall, A., & Gilbert, J. (2015). *Motivational Interviewing Competency Assessment (MICA)* [Coding manual]. Retrieved from http://micacoding.com/manual

Jobes, D. A. (2017). Clinical assessment and treatment of suicidal risk: A critique of contemporary care and CAMS as a possible remedy. *Practice Innovations, 2*(4), 207–220.

Kabat-Zinn, J. (1994). *Wherever you go, there you are: Mindfulness meditation in everyday life.* New York: Hyperion/Hachette Book Group.

Kovacs, M., & Beck, A. T. (1977). The wish to die and the wish to live in attempted suicides. *Journal of Clinical Psychology, 33*(2), 361–365.

Marcus, M., Westra, H. A., Angus, L., & Kertes, A. (2011). Client experiences of motivational interviewing for generalized anxiety disorder: A qualitative analysis. *Psychotherapy Research, 21*(4), 447–461.

Martin, T., Christopher, P. J., Houck, J. M., & Moyers, T. B. (2011). The structure of client language and drinking outcomes in project match. *Psychology of Addictive Behaviors, 25*(3), 439–445.

Martino, S., Carroll, K., Kostas, D., Perkins, J., & Rounsaville, B. (2002). Dual diagnosis motivational interviewing: A modification of motivational interviewing for substance-abusing patients with psychotic disorders. *Journal of Substance Abuse Treatment, 23*(4), 297–308.

Miller, I. W., Gaudiano, B. A., & Weinstock, L. M. (2016). The coping long term with active suicide program: Description and pilot data. *Suicide & Life-threatening Behavior, 46*(6), 752–761.

Miller, W. R. (Ed.). (2004). Combined behavioral intervention manual: A clinical research guide for therapists treating people with alcohol abuse and dependence. *COMBINE Monograph Series* (Vol. 1). Bethesda, MD: National Institute on Alcohol Abuse and Alcoholism. DHHS No. 04-5288.

Miller, W. R., Benefield, R. G., & Tonigan, J. S. (1993). Enhancing motivation for change in problem drinking: A controlled comparison of two therapist styles. *Journal of Consulting and Clinical Psychology, 61*(3), 455–461.

Miller, W. R., C'de Baca, J., Matthews, D. B. & Wilbourne, P. L. (2001). *Personal values card sort.* Retrieved from https://casaa.unm.edu/inst/Personal%20Values%20Card%20Sort.pdf

Miller, W. R., & Mount, K. A. (2001). A small study of training in motivational interviewing: Does one workshop change clinician and client behavior? *Behavioural and Cognitive Psychotherapy, 29,* 457–471.

Miller, W. R., Forcehimes, A. A., & Zweben, A. (2019). *Treating addictions: A guide for professionals* (2nd ed.). New York, NY: Guilford Press.

Miller, W. R., & Moyers, T. B. (2021). *Effective psychotherapists: Clinical skills that improve client outcomes.* New York: Guilford Press.

Miller, W. R., & Moyers, T. B. (2017). Motivational interviewing and the clinical science of Carl Rogers. *Journal of Consulting and Clinical Psychology, 85*(8), 757–766.

Miller, W. R., & Moyers, T. B. (2006). Eight stages in learning motivational interviewing. *Journal of Teaching in the Addictions, 5*(1), 3–17.

Miller, W. R., & Rollnick, S. (1991). *Motivational interviewing: Preparing people to change addictive behavior.* New York, NY: Guilford Press.

Miller, W. R., & Rollnick, S. (2013). *Motivational interviewing* (3rd ed.). New York, NY: Guilford Press.

Miller, W. R., & Rose, G. S. (2015). Motivational interviewing and decisional balance: Contrasting responses to client ambivalence. *Behavioural and Cognitive Psychotherapy, 43*(2), 129–141.

Miller, W. R., Yahne, C. E., Moyers, T. B., Martinez, J., & Pirritano, M. (2004). A randomized trial of methods to help clinicians learn motivational interviewing. *Journal of Consulting and Clinical Psychology, 72*(6), 1050–1062.

Motivational Interviewing Network of Trainers. (2018). *Creating a motivational interviewing learning community: guidance from the motivational interviewing network of trainers.* Retrieved from: https://motivationalinterviewing.org/sites/default/files/learning_communities_guidelines_june_2019.pdf

Moyers, T. B., & Martino, S. (2006). What's important in my life: The personal goals and values card sorting task for individuals with schizophrenia. Retrieved from https://casaa.unm.edu/inst/Values%20Card%20Sorting%20Task%20for%20Individuals%20with%20Schizophrenia.pdf

Moyers, T. B., & Miller, W. R. (2013). Brief report: Is low therapist empathy toxic? *Psychology of Addictive Behaviors, 27*(3), 878–884.

Moyers, T. B., Miller, W. R., & Hendrickson, S. M. L. (2005). How does motivational interviewing work? Therapist interpersonal skill predicts client involvement within motivational interviewing sessions. *Journal of Consulting and Clinical Psychology, 73*(4), 590–598.

Moyers, T. B., Rowell, L. N., Manuel, J. K., Ernst, D., & Houck, J. M. (2016). The Motivational Interviewing Treatment Integrity Code (MITI 4): Rationale, preliminary reliability and validity. *Journal of Substance Abuse Treatment, 65,* 36–42.

Naar, S., & Flynn, H. (2015). Motivational interviewing treatment of depression. In H. Arkowitz, W. R., Miller, & S. Rollnick (Eds.), *Motivational interviewing in the treatment of psychological problems* (2nd ed.). New York, NY: Guilford Press.

Naar, S., & Safren, S. A. (2017). *Motivational interviewing and CBT: Combining strategies for maximum effectiveness.* New York, NY: Guilford Press.

Nashölm, C. (2006, December 2). *Exploring ambivalence—more than a decisional balance?* [PowerPoint slides]. Retrieved from http://www.monarchsystem.com/wp-content/uploads/2012/06/Exploring-ambivalence-by-Christina-N%C3%A4sholm.pdf

National Alliance on Mental Illness (n.d.). *Tobacco and smoking.* Retrieved from https://www.nami.org/learn-more/mental-health-public-policy/tobacco-and-smoking

Neff, K. D., & Dahm, K. A. (2015) Self-compassion: What it is, what it does, and how it relates to mindfulness. In B. D. Ostafin, M. D. Robinson, & B. P. Meier (Eds.), *Handbook of mindfulness and self-regulation* (pp. 121–137). New York, NY: Springer.

Norcross, J. C., & Wampold, B. E. (2011). Evidence-based therapy relationships: Research conclusions and clinical practices. *Psychotherapy, 48*(1), 98–102.

Posner, K., Brown, G. K., Stanley, B., Brent, D. A., Yershova, K. V., Oquendo, M. A., … Mann, J. J. (2011). The Columbia-Suicide Severity Rating Scale: Initial validity and internal consistency findings from three multisite studies with adolescents and adults. *The American Journal of Psychiatry, 168*(12), 1266–77.

Resnicow, K., & McMaster, F. (2012). Motivational interviewing: Moving from why to how with autonomy support. *International Journal of Behavioral Nutrition and Physical Activity, 9*(19).

Richardson, K., & Barkham, M. (2017). Recovery from depression: A systematic review of perceptions and associated factors. *Journal of Mental Health, 29*(1), 103–115.

Robinson, J. D., & Heritage, J. (2006). Physician opening questions and patient satisfaction. *Patient Education and Counseling, 60*(3), 279–285.

Rogers, C. R. (1980). *A way of being.* Boston: Houghton Mifflin Harcourt.

Rogers, C. R. (1965). *Client-centered therapy.* New York, NY: Houghton-Mifflin.

Rogers, C. R. (1959). A theory of therapy, personality, and interpersonal relationships as developed in the client-centered framework. In S. Koch (Ed.), *Psychology: A study of a science* (Vol. 3, pp. 184–256). New York, NY: McGraw-Hill.

Sijercic, I., Button, M. L., Westra, H. A., & Hara, K. M. (2016). The interpersonal context of client motivational language in cognitive-behavioral therapy. *Psychotherapy (Chic)*, *53*(1), 13–21.

Simon, G. E., Rutter, C. M., Peterson, D., Oliver, M., Whiteside, U., Operskalski, B., & Ludman, E. J. (2013). Does response on the PHQ-9 Depression Questionnaire predict subsequent suicide attempt or suicide death? *Psychiatric Services*, *64*(12), 1195–1202.

Sobell, M. B., & Sobell, L. C. (1993). *Problem drinkers: A guided self-change treatment.* New York: Guilford Press.

Suppes, T. Leverich, G. S., Keck, P. E., Nolen, W. A., Denicoff, K. D., Altshuler, L. L., … Post, R. M. (2001). The Stanley Foundation Bipolar Treatment Outcome Network. II. Demographics and illness characteristics of the first 261 patients. *Journal of Affective Disorders*, *67*(1–3), 45–59.

Tondo, L., Vázquez, G. H., & Baldessarini, R. J. (2017). Depression and mania in bipolar disorder. *Current Neuropharmacology*, *15*(3), 353–358.

Tondora, J. (2013, December). *The person-centered recovery plan: A tool for recovery-oriented systems orientation* [PowerPoint slides]. Retrieved from https://www.spokanecounty.org/DocumentCenter/View/22445/Tondora-EXPANDED-skills-training-Spokane-Recovery-Planning-12-2013

Topor, A., Bøe, T. D., Larsen, I. B. (2018). Small things, micro-affirmations and helpful professionals everyday recovery-orientated practices according to persons with mental health problems. *Community Mental Health Journal*, *54*(8), 1212–1220.

Truax, C. B., & Carkhuff, R. R. (1967). *Toward effective counseling and psychotherapy.* Chicago, IL: Aldine.

Undrill, G., & Toogood, H. (2018). *Advanced communication skills.* Retrieved from www.guyundrill.com/assets/handbook2018v1.5.pdf

Valle, S. K. (1981). Interpersonal functioning of alcoholism counselors and treatment outcome. *Journal of Studies on Alcohol*, *42*(9), 783–790.

Veseth, M., Binder, P. E., Borg, M., & Davidson, L.(2013). How I found out I had a bipolar disorder: A reflexive-collaborative exploration of the process of identifying that one is struggling with a severe mental health problem. *Qualitative Studies*, *4*(1), 21–38.

Wagner, C. C., & Ingersoll, K. S., (2013). Applications of motivational interviewing. *Motivational interviewing in groups.* Guilford Press.

Westra, H. A. (2012). *Motivational interviewing in the treatment of anxiety.* New York, NY: Guilford Press.

Westra, H. A., & Arkowitz, H. (2010). Combining motivational interviewing and cognitive-behavioral therapy to increase treatment efficacy for generalized anxiety disorder. In D. Sookman & R. L. Leahy (Eds.), *Treatment resistant anxiety disorders: Resolving impasses to symptom remission* (pp. 199–231). New York, NY: Routledge/Taylor & Francis Group.

Westra, H. A., & Constantino, M. J. (2019). Integrative treatment of anxiety. In J. D. Norcross & M. R. Goldfried (Eds.), *Handbook of psychotherapy integration* (pp. 284–302). New York, NY: Oxford University Press.

Westra, H. A., Constantino, M. J., & Aviram, A. (2011). The impact of alliance ruptures on client outcome expectations in cognitive behavioural therapy for generalized anxiety disorder. *Psychotherapy Research*, *21*, 472–481.

Zerler, H. (2007). Motivational interviewing and suicidality. In H. Arkowitz, H. A. Westra, W. R. Miller, & S. Rollnick (Eds.), *Motivational interviewing in the treatment of psychological problems* (pp. 173–193). New York, NY: Guilford Press.

Zuckoff, A., Swartz, H. A., & Grote, N. K. (2015). Motivational interviewing as a prelude to psychotherapy of depressed women. In H. Arkowitz, W. R., Miller, & S. Rollnick (Eds.), *Motivational interviewing in the treatment of psychological problems* (2nd ed.; pp. 136–169). New York, NY: Guilford Press.

APPENDIX
SUICIDE RISK RESOURCES

SCREENING

Ask Suicide Screening Questions (ASQ)

https://www.nimh.nih.gov/research/research-conducted-at-nimh/asq-toolkit-materials/index.shtml

Columbia-Suicide Severity Rating Scale (C-SSRS; Posner et al., 2011)

https://cssrs.columbia.edu/wp-content/uploads/C-SSRS_Pediatric-SLC_11.14.16.pdf

Patient Health Questionnaire-9

http://www.med.umich.edu/1info/FHP/practiceguides/depress/phq-9.pdf

Patient Safety Screener 3 (PSS-3)

https://www.emnet-usa.org/wp-content/uploads/PatientSafetyScreener.pdf

SUICIDE RISK ASSESSMENT AND TREATMENT INTERVENTION INFORMATION

Department of Veteran's Affairs/Department of Defense (2013), VA/DoD Clinical practice guideline for assessment and management of patients at risk for suicide

https://www.mentalhealth.va.gov/docs/va029assessmentguide.pdf

National Suicide Prevention Lifeline

https://suicidepreventionlifeline.org/

Suicide Prevention Resource Center

http://www.sprc.org/

U.S. Department of Health and Human Services, Substance Abuse and Mental Health Services Administration (SAMHSA)

https://www.samhsa.gov/

VA Mental Health *Suicide Risk Assessment Guide* (2018)

https://www.mentalhealth.va.gov/docs/suicide_risk_assessment_reference_guide.pdf

Made in the USA
Middletown, DE
10 July 2024

57103576R00192